FROM
BEHIND
THE
MASK

TULSA NIGHTWRITERS

***An Anthology
Inspired by the
COVID-19 Pandemic of 2020***

Cover Design – Faith Wylie
Publishing Coordinator – Sharon Kizziah-Holmes

Paperback-Press
an imprint of A & S Publishing
A & S Holmes, Inc.

ISBN -13: 978-1-951772-48-2

CONTENTS

INTRODUCTION

By Cindy Rose

This anthology was conceived during the COVID-19 Pandemic of 2020, and written by members of The Tulsa NightWriters' Club. It represents a collection of writers reaching out *From Behind the Mask* to share their imaginings and accounts of living while coping with the pandemic.

With ages ranging from fourteen into their eighties, our members comprise all walks of life, professions, and types of writing. Before the pandemic, we met monthly in person to hear dynamic speakers and visit with friends. In March, 2020, the virus forced us to suspend in-person meetings, and the NightWriters' Board of Directors moved the meetings online via the Zoom platform.

Still, the Board wanted to do more to salvage 2020. This anthology, which offers a publishing credit, was undertaken as a project to involve the members during the quarantine. While not a substitute for mixing and mingling monthly with our friends, *From Behind the Mask* is something tangible the participating authors can hold onto and give away, treasure and pass on to future generations as a witness to a time like no other since the 1918 Spanish Flu Pandemic—one hundred years ago.

As you read the writings included in these pages, it is our hope that the stories, poems and essays will transport you away from your own troubles, and allow you to view these trying times through others' eyes.

***

From Behind the Mask is an anthology that has been produced under the guidance of the Tulsa NightWriters' Club. One of Oklahoma's oldest writing organizations, it has been in existence since the 1960's and welcomes writers of all ages, regardless their preferred genre or level of experience.

For more information about meetings, conferences, or other gatherings please visit their website at: tulsanightwriters.wordpress.com

Days Remembered

by **Derek Bullard**

Do you remember where you were when...?

Actually, I don't *specifically remember* where I was when President John F. Kennedy was assassinated in Dallas. Not uncommon as most folks don't remember things which happened around them at age two. However, I do *know exactly* where I was because my mom remembers, and she told me.

Sixty miles north, sitting on the floor in a living room in Whitesboro, Texas. Playing with toys and not a care in the world.

But the world changed a bit that day.

Ironically, it happened as Mom watched her favorite soap opera, *As the World Turns.*

Ten minutes in, at about 12:40 p.m., the soapy drama was bubbling. Nancy Hughes, played by Helen Wagner, had just told Grandpa (Santos Ortega) that her son, Bob, had invited his ex-wife, the scheming Lisa, and their young son, Tom, to Thanksgiving dinner.

After his initial shock, Grandpa ventured, "That was real nice of the boy."

"And I've thought about it," Nancy said, "and I gave it a great deal of thought, Grandpa —"[1]

---

[1] https://www.nytimes.com/2013/11/24/arts/television/as-the-world-turns-interrupted-by-kennedys-shooting.html?smid=em-share accessed 7-15-2020

There are certain benchmarks in time. Occasions such as birthdays, weddings, and the loss of a loved one. Engrams stamped like souvenirs of life's journey in the recesses of our minds. Historical events serve the same purpose.

At that instant, Nancy and Grandpa were wiped off the screen, replaced by the words "CBS News Bulletin" slide and the urgent voice of Walter Cronkite.[2]

November 22, 1963

The beloved and trusted anchorman announced that President John F. Kennedy was seriously injured in a shooting in Dallas, Texas. (Years later I would learn one of my uncles had shaken the President's hand at Love Field and another of my uncles on the Dallas police force had been tasked with keeping reporters away from a point of interest. Mom and Dad were also watching live television coverage the next day and saw Jack Ruby fatally shoot Lee Harvey Oswald while in police custody.)

As the world continues to turn, there are many more days I recall. Each memory reminds me of how the world constantly changes. Sometimes subtly. Sometimes drastically.

How normal days become not normal.
How plans are disrupted.
Political climates sway.
Lost lives.
Lives taken.
Hopes dashed.
Dreams unfulfilled.
Economies wrecked.
Nothing new under the sun.[3]
Not since Adam & Eve yielded to temptation has it been any different.

---

[2] Ibid
[3] Ecclesiastes 1:9 NKJ *The thing that hath been, it is that which shall be; and that which is done is that which shall be done: and there is no new thing under the sun.*

I remember a great day of riding horses with my family in the mountains near Gunnison, Colorado. The cool evening concluded with a chuckwagon supper around a huge campfire. The pleasant aroma of flame cooked steak and beans on tin plates. Night noises from the surrounding pines. Subdued conversations.

Times were good for a boy my age.

Man had traveled to the Moon and made footprints in the dust.

Those of us who saw those space explorers on television remembered those days as the Moon and stars, so clear and close to our camp at this elevation, looked as if they were within easy reach.

A president had greeted the astronauts on their return from afar, a triumph for the nation.

Now, on this peaceful evening, a moment of disgrace for the same said nation.

"Hey, turn it up!" Someone pointed at a guy with a radio. "Turn it up so we can all hear."

Maybe thirty or forty people perked an ear.

"Now, from the White House," the newsman stated solemnly, "the President of the United States."

August 8, 1974

"Good evening. This is the 37th time I have spoken to you from this office..."

Richard Nixon's resignation speech lasted 16 minutes.

Pre-season High School football in the hot summer sun of Lindsay, Oklahoma. They called it two-a-days because for a full week we slept, we practiced, we ate lunch, we practiced again, we ran, and then willed our sore bodies home and slept some more.

After one of the practices, the team stopped on the sidewalk outside the gym. We stood by a narrow alley-like street which traversed between the field and the school. The stench of sweat negated the air of fresh mown grass. Our head coach arrived to unlock the door. We turned our attention from him at the squall of tires as a car sped by at top speed. The passenger waved and yelled something from his window.

August 16, 1977
"Elvis is dead!"

Fast forward to college days on the campus of The University of Oklahoma in Norman. I lived in a third-floor dorm with no air conditioner. The freshmen had started a strange afternoon routine of gathering in the common room to watch *Mr. Roger's Neighborhood*. I still don't know why this group of guys were so mesmerized by Fred Rogers singing about it being a beautiful day in the neighborhood.

Elsewhere in the world, the neighborhood was ugly.

Fifty-two embassy hostages were still being held in Iran. Diplomacy had failed.

All the young men in that common room had signed up with Selective Service. We didn't know if the crises meant war or not. We feared someone might strike a match to the tinder of stalemate and set the Middle East on fire.

April 24, 1980
A PBS newscaster interrupted Mr. Rogers' happy day to tell us about how rescue helicopters were downed in a sandstorm. As U.S. forces prepared to withdraw, one of the helicopters had crashed into a transport aircraft. Bad luck? Bad planning? Who knew?

Although I was prepared to go if called, the draft was not enacted. The hostages were released on January 20, 1981 after 444 days.

While on vacation with my parents, I stood on the side of Interstate 5 somewhere near the Washington/Oregon state line. Quickly changing lenses on my 35mm camera, I tried not to get run over by the other cars swerving off the road onto the shoulder to see what everyone was pointing at. Amid all the honking and skidding, I managed to snag a pretty cool photo of the volcanic plume.

August 7, 1980
The 7th major eruption of Mt. St. Helens.

As I said, my dorm room had no AC. So, to catch any breeze

possible, the windows stayed open most of the day and night. This time the television, a tiny black and white model, sat with its power off. As did the radio. Homework time at my small desk, wedged between a twin bed and a closet door. From the sidewalk below, as if from an old-time town crier came a loud announcement which echoed off the building.

March 30, 1981
"President Reagan's been shot!"

My family spent a week in Cancun, Mexico. Swam in the ocean, toured some Mayan ruins, and had a wonderful time in the sun. As we prepared to fly home, one day was paradise and the next day was, "Uh, how long are we going to be stranded here?"

August 5, 1981
The Professional Air-Traffic Controllers Association workers had been on strike and refused to return to work. In response President Reagan fired the 11,345 striking air traffic controllers who had ignored the order.

Having been born at the onset of the 1960s, I always felt a kinship with the space program. From the early days of NASA up to the launch of the Space Shuttle.

I sat at my desk doing some paperwork for an oilfield rental company in McAlester, Oklahoma. An average workday. Boring. One of the shop workers came in for a cup of coffee and casually shared some news he'd just heard on the radio in the back of the building.

January 28, 1986
"Hey, did you hear the Challenger blew up?"

Strangely that tragedy set in motion a complete change of direction in my life. I'd grown tired of the job, working 24/7 and having been given a pager so they could find me on weekends. I went home at the end of the day, sad and depressed at the loss of the seven astronauts. Soon I'd be in my living room watching the replay of the explosion. But before that happened, as I crawled from my pickup in the driveway, the landlord of our rental house approached to tell me he had decided to sell the property. Could I have the place cleaned up for the buyers to walk through tomorrow? Oh, and I'd need to vacate as the month-to-month lease expired in just a day or two.

To say the least, with the mood I was in, this ultimatum from left field didn't set well and I told him what I thought of his short notice idea.

The next day, I talked to the owner of a rental one lot over, and with the promise to paint three rooms and a nice deposit, we transferred everything from one house to the other. About a week after that, and having finished with the painting, I'd applied for a job in a newspaper ad and it led to a great interview in Oklahoma City. Since I told the interviewer how most of my belongings were already in packing boxes and ready to go, he hired me for a job in Lawton, Oklahoma as an assistant manager of a toy store. (I later heard the original house didn't sell for about three years.) We'd probably never had made such a drastic change if I hadn't been upset over the shuttle tragedy and ambushed in that driveway. Oh, and I had to forfeit the deposit to the second rental.

The job in Lawton led to a management position with the same company in Tulsa.

Sitting with my wife in Goldie's Patio Grill on 31st Street, listening to the radio, not playing the usual music, but relaying reports of the beginning of something massive.

August 2, 1990
Operation Desert Shield in Iraq.

My Dad had briefly met David Koresh when he helped drill a water well on the Branch Davidian property in Waco, Texas.

April 19, 1993
In my living room watching as the compound burned to the ground.

I continued to manage the toy store.
Over time I made acquaintances with many older folks who

mall walked in the early hours of the day.

One morning, as I manned the front of the store alone, one of the usually friendly faces passed by. His manner appeared different. His shoulders sagged and he looked at the floor.

With a weak wave, he glanced over at me.

April 19, 1995

"Boy, that's a bad thing down in Oklahoma City, isn't it?"

He didn't elaborate, just walked on. I surveyed the mall. Strangely empty and no one to ask if they knew anything.

We had a small television in the store to show video games. It didn't have an antenna. I fashioned one out of something and in a moment tuned in a wavy newscast from the state capital. On the screen were firetrucks, ambulances, police cars, and in the background half a building and a huge pile of rubble.

Two things happened just before my Dad lost his fight with cancer. He was in the Sherman, Texas hospital and we were fortunate enough to be with him on his birthday and when he passed just a few days later. Two events were constantly in the background as it seems when you're in and out of a hospital waiting room the television is always on.

July 17 & July 27, 1996

TWA Flight 800, a Boeing 747-100, exploded and crashed into the Atlantic Ocean twelve minutes after takeoff from John F. Kennedy International Airport in New York.

A domestic terrorist pipe bombing in the Centennial Olympic Park during the 1996 Summer Olympics in Atlanta.

It's interesting how all of these things came to my attention by way of television, radio, the yelling of strangers, the conversations of friends and family, plus the occasional direct observation.

Again, in my living room in Tulsa watching late night television with my wife as the show is interrupted.

7

August 31, 1997
"Diana, Princess of Wales, has been in a car crash while fleeing the paparazzi."

I had left the job in the mall and after a brief year in marketing took a position with the Gatesway Foundation, teaching employment skills to people with disabilities. As a job coach I had a crew of six and another job coach keeping two parking garages clean near the Doubletree Hotel at 61st & Yale. All morning we walked a mile or two up and down inside the multi-story structure and when lunch time approached we boarded our van and drove out of the garage to head back over to the break room. As the radio caught the signal, instead of the usual music, we heard somber news coverage. Without context it didn't make any sense.

September 11, 2001
"The second tower is collapsing."
The next day, as we stood on top of the garage and gazed into a sky void of planes, I remarked to the other coach what I felt on this particular morning. We were looking at a different world. We were in the same shoes our grandparents stood in on December 8, 1941. Trying to make sense of a senseless attack. Wondering if anything would ever be the same?

My wife and I often traveled on my birthday back to Whitesboro, to be with my mom. The weekend fell a bit earlier this time and we were about halfway through breakfast when another uncle, who had been strangely silent, cleared his throat. "Did you see the news this morning?"
"No."

February 1, 2003
Nearly two hundred miles south of us, the Space Shuttle Columbia had disintegrated on reentry in the sky over Texas.

What, you are wondering, does all this have to do with the COVID-19 pandemic?
You see, I remember where I was.
Sitting, again with my wife, in the Village Inn on Harvard in

Tulsa. We'd been served our breakfast and noticed the waitress was watching a newscast on the television in the corner. We couldn't hear anything, but we could read the scrawl along the bottom. I'd told my wife earlier in the week about a new phrase I'd heard and expected to hear a lot more. "Social distancing." I thought it was an oxymoron.

March 17, 2020

On this date there were seventeen confirmed cases of COVID-19 in Oklahoma.

The mayor announced an executive order closing restaurants, with the exception of take-out and drive-through, in the city - effective 11:59 p.m.

All the waitresses looked distraught.

A cook came out of the kitchen carrying an assortment of frying pans. "I'm out of here," he said to no one in particular. "See ya when this is all over!"

It was supposed to last fifteen days.

Our church stopped meeting for services.

We missed being together Easter, Mother's Day, Memorial Day, Father's Day, and Vacation Bible School.

Two weekend conferences I had planned to attend - Canceled. A week-long conference my wife had paid in advance to go to in San Antonio – Canceled. A trip to Branson to see a show we'd been given tickets to last Christmas – Canceled. Tulsa NightWriters meetings and Toastmaster meetings – now conducted via video conferencing.

I can't go visit my mom.

As I write this, we are in the fifth month of those fifteen days and it's been reported the virus is spiking again. Some restaurants have reopened, but I've seen at least six of my favorites apparently closed for good. The school year ended abruptly. Oklahoma's Governor announced he'd tested positive for the virus. If you go into a bank, they want you to keep your mask on. Movie theaters are dark and it's weird the poster holders are empty. Office buildings sit vacant as folks work from home.

Strangely, traffic still seems the same.

If someone is smiling, you can't tell because it's behind their mask.

We've all tried to cope with this thing in different ways.

The loss of life to date is tragic.

After being around someone who ended up in the hospital (he recovered), my wife and I were tested. Swab up the nose. Felt like when you get water in your sinus after jumping feet first into a swimming pool. Tests came back negative. We were relieved and have a new perspective.

Since the pandemic started we've had reports of "Murder Hornets", a civil unrest, a sand cloud heading our way from the Sahara, a possible case of the Bubonic Plague in China, and a retail coin shortage, all during the taking of the census, a presidential election, and the hoarding of toilet paper.

Yet the world still turns as it still did in 1961.

...the live telecast of "As the World Turns" No. 1,995 (there was no title) remains frozen in time as a last semblance of normalcy before the face of television changed permanently. The very ordinariness of Wagner's scene —[4]

When things start to feel ordinary again something else happens.

The old normalcy cedes to the new normalcy as sure as night cedes to day.

How do I deal with it?

Faith and Trust. With time, study, and prayer - life's journey moves forward.

Let us hear the conclusion of the whole matter: Fear God, and keep his commandments: for this is the whole duty of man.[5]

Two songs come to mind. We can choose which lines up best with our mindset.

---

[4] https://www.nytimes.com/2013/11/24/arts/television/as-the-world-turns-interrupted-by-kennedys-shooting.html?smid=em-share accessed 7-15-2020

[5] Ecclesiastes 12:13 KJV

It's the End of the World as We Know It (And I Feel Fine) by the American rock band R.E.M.

Or, *This World is Not My Home (I'm Just a Passing Through),* a traditional hymn.

For me, it's the latter.

So, what's next for the world?

Who knows?

Perhaps we'll remember where we were when…

DEREK BULLARD

●●●

Derek, an award-winning author, screenwriter, and speaker has published five books and his articles/stories have been read around the world. In 2018 Derek served as NightWriters' Vice President and Chaired their "Craft of Writing" Conference. In 2020, before the pandemic, he conducted a Speechcraft Workshop where several NightWriters improved their public speaking skills. Also, in 2020, Derek received recognition from Toastmasters International as a Distinguished Toastmaster. Writing under the pseudonym Ira Amos, he is currently working on the second novel in his Arcadia Vyne mystery series. Derek lives in Tulsa with wife LaDonna and family of cats. www.jameskaypublishing.com

Cowboys Buying Belt Buckles in Tiffany's

by **Gerald Carter**

The whole world's in flux.

You pay your money.

You take your chances.

Wear your Stetson with your tux.

These times are getting stranger

The strong trampling on the weak.

So, buy your belts at Tiffany's.

Sell your souls at the five and dime.

And those who had the virus?

Well, there's really not the time

For much maudlin despairs.

See, it's the economy, Stupid,

That deserves "our thoughts and prayers."

From the Underbelly of the Pandemic 2020

by **Gerald Carter**

Crazy Times and crazy people

With Goliaths (corona-style) stalking the earth.

Gonna take more than a slingshot this time!

Hope we outlast 'em (people and virus) I guess.

They really are dinosaurs

Right before the meteor of Reality strikes.

That's my view from the underbelly.

Dark Nature, you're still there.

Crawling on your belly through the slime.

Clouds cover the sun, but it's not gone,

Just unseen.

We're all in a battle

That's been waged for so long…Eons!

What's possible. That's what I want.

Nothing fancy, so to speak.

I have a peasant's taste.

So basic gruel will do just fine

And a quiet place to breathe.

GERALD CARTER

•••

Gerald W. Carter is married to his wife, Nancy, and currently lives in Broken Arrow, Oklahoma. He is a retired Licensed Professional Counselor, Licensed Alcohol Drug Counselor and National Board Certified Counselor. He has worked in hospitals, a prison, both public and private behavioral health clinics and had a small private practice for 16 years. He and Nancy together have 4 sons and 6 grandchildren. He was born in Lebanon, Missouri and obtained a B A in Psychology and a MS in Guidance and Counseling at what is now called Missouri State University in Springfield, Missouri. He has been a member of several writing groups and has previously independently published a book of poetry called My Year of Living Poetically. He has written mainly poetry, but also written a novelette and contributed to the State of Oklahoma's prison manual on stress management

Pieces of White

by **Mary Coley**

amantha leaned against the cool glass of the window. Fuzzy quiet. No screams of grief. No whispers. Her doctor had promised that in time she'd forget all that. Forget COVID. How?

She watched the dark asphalt road undulate through the unfamiliar green landscape. Fresh earthy scent, the air of growing things—farmland—breezed through the car's air vents. Not the auto-exhaust scent of the airport they'd left an hour ago, and the city surrounding it.

Looking out into the jigsaw puzzle landscape of farms, and trees, and fields growing crops, the world swayed and blurred.

Thank God she wasn't driving. She couldn't concentrate. Couldn't stop the waking nightmare, couldn't sleep. Had no appetite, no wants, no needs. No emotions.

"Your bath is ready, Samantha. You need to wash your hair. Clean your fingernails. You're a mess. You've got to move on. Have a good cry." The voice in her head belonged to her mother. She'd been gone for twenty years, and Dad for twenty-five. And she still grieved for them.

She wanted to ask someone: Exactly how do you learn to move on? And how do you make yourself cry? COVID had not made her ill, it had stolen her emotions over days and weeks. A numbing stillness filled her. She'd shed no tears, not even when white shrouds covered the still bodies of her daughter and her husband.

Samantha glanced through the passenger window. *Leave the driving to Liam.* She'd never been a particularly good driver, too easily distracted by the world outside to keep her eyes on the road. She would never drive again. What was the point of going anywhere, doing anything? In an uncertain future, she could get COVID; could be gone in an instant.

In the distance, on the edge of the field, a pair of deer grazed. She grabbed the strap of the camera bag on the floorboard at her feet and jerked it into her lap. She flipped the latch and pulled out the digital camera. A pile of printed photos she'd stuffed into the bag fell out onto the car floor. She left them there; she had to snap this shot. For Audrey. The camera lens clicked.

Her daughter, Audrey, had taken those photos, little minute memories, over the past year in photography class. At the time, the photos seemed mundane, except to her daughter. After the funeral, Samantha studied each one and wondered why Audrey chose to take the photograph. What did it mean to her? Why had the subject or the colors caught her eye? She wished she'd studied those photos and asked questions all those months ago. She wished she'd known the woman Audrey was becoming.

The beautiful deer watched the car pass. An instant later, Samantha strained to see the animals, but couldn't. Curled up in the woods, hidden in the ferns, their fawns were safe. The little ones would graze, grow, and become big-eyed deer like their parents. She'd remember them, she had them on film.

Samantha bent to grab the pictures scattered on the floorboard. In the top photo, white shapes fluttered in the wind. Where had Audrey been when she took it? Who hung their laundry on lines anymore? And who wore only white? It seemed an anomaly, and she wanted to know. But Audrey wasn't here to ask. Now, white meant disease, and death, and futures vanished like a wisp of a cloud. Samantha clutched the photos to her heart.

Outside the car window, a cluster of buildings moved past. The digital camera had attached itself to her hand, become part of her. She pulled it to her face and snapped a photo of a lone white-washed stucco home, set back a block from the two-lane road. A family home, she imagined, once inhabited by two adults and three children. Her imagination filled in a story: the children had grown up and gone off to school, leaving behind two middle-aged adults. The man, a part-time farmer, worked in the town hardware store five miles back. The woman taught in the town's grade school. Retirement was a decade away for both, and they missed their children. They wanted grandchildren, but none had arrived.

The imagined story merged with her own life when Samantha realized dully that her own grandchildren would never arrive.

Although she leaned to keep the house within the viewfinder of her camera, a green field and grazing horses replaced it. She snapped a photo, expecting a story about horses to fill her head, but nothing came. She lowered the camera to her lap.

"Lots to take pictures of," Liam, her brother, said. She stole a quick glance at him, at the red whiskers poking from his cheeks and the dimple in his chin. His bare face registered. Shouldn't he be wearing a mask? To protect her. Samantha sucked in a quick breath and touched her own bare jawline. Maskless. What if she had brought the COVID with her, to their home? She considered unbuckling her seat belt and leaping from the car.

Liam stared ahead. A spot of brown paint on his right thigh marred brilliant white coveralls. Her sister-in-law Kate would have to work to get that stain out, but then, what else did she have to do?

"I'm glad you came to us for a bit, Sam. And Kate is too. We're glad to have you."

She wondered about that. A middle-aged woman dropped into their laps. One more mouth to feed. A disruption for her only brother and his wife. Well, she'd make sure not to disrupt their lives. Not to make noise, not to alter any plans. Unlike what they might expect.

A bitter taste filled her mouth. She wouldn't think about life before COVID. Samantha settled back in the seat and let the stillness cover her.

She'd decided not to stay long with Liam. She'd wander into the hills one evening, like Jasper had done, like any good old dog would do so no one had to see its end.

The asphalt road topped a hill and dove into a green valley. Her camera came up and she pressed the button. The camera made a flurry of clicks. The valley looked like a place a fairy might live, a fairy that granted wishes.

Samantha straightened and pressed her palm against the window. Ten years ago, if Audrey had been traveling with her, she might have made up a story about the valley. She considered the beginning of the story ... Last year, before COVID, the fairy awarded three wishes to children who'd lost their parents. But their wishes to the fairy—that the authorities would not send the children to an orphanage or foster home—had come true. Miraculously, the lost family members returned. They lived happily ever after.

Samantha risked a small smile for the sake of her little-girl heart. If only wishes could come true. Her heart was too badly broken to hope, much less believe, in wishes.

"Pretty, eh? Wait'll you see the valley beyond our house." Liam scratched his head, his fingers digging into the scalp beneath his turning-gray red hair.

'Pretty' was subjective, wasn't it? 'Pretty' could be rough, brash, and noisy if that's what a person preferred. She thought about Audrey's photos. 'Pretty' could be a moonless midnight full of stars or fluttering white shapes in the blue sky. 'Pretty' could be a red rose in a bush of green thorns, or a purple jellyfish on brown sand.

The route curved into a forest of trees. They loomed overhead, hiding the blue sky and the clumps of gray and white clouds. The cool air coming through the vents smelled of pine, and damp earth, moss, and ferns. She peered into the forest; the trees flashed by. Barely visible between the trees, sat a cabin. The camera clicked and once again, she imagined a story.

A lonely man lived there. He had lost his sweetheart to a disease when he was a young man. He'd gone off to war; she sickened and died while he was gone. He never loved again. A woodcarver, he sold his creations in gift shops and at county fairs, little figurines carved and painted and signed on the bottom with an A, for his name, 'Albert.' A, for 'Alone.'

"Kinda gloomy in here." Liam interrupted her imaginings as he drove deep into the forest. He flicked on the car lights, and when a few drops of rain splattered the windshield, he turned on the wipers. The rain smeared the glass. He peered through it, and the car slowed.

The pavement dropped into a deep cleft of a glen; looming shadows ate the lush forest. "It'll be bright and sunny by the time we reach the house. From the porch, you can see the lake. And there's a boat dock with a cafe. We'll go there soon, and you can meet my buddy Johnny, he owns the place. Loves the lake, loves the solitude."

Liam returned his focus to driving and the dark forest road

revealed by the car's headlights. The blackness dropped like a hood over her head. She sucked a quick breath of the dank, heavy air that swooshed from the vents.

Liam's hand touched her shoulder. "Just another minute, Sis. We're almost out. Not my favorite place, either."

The camera felt heavy in her lap. No picture to take here. Nothing Samantha wanted to see again. Nothing that made her want to speak again. Or laugh. Or even smile. She closed her eyes. The darkness hugged her, squeezed her throat. She gasped for breath.

Her brother patted her leg.

Cold swept out of the air vents. She shivered.

She focused on the rhythmic sound of the tires on the pavement. Zhhh. Zhhh. Thump. Zhhh. Zhhh. Thump. Zhhh. Zhhh. Thump. Zhhh. Zhhh—

"There now, see the blue sky ahead. It's all right now," Liam soothed.

Samantha opened her eyes, off balance. She wasn't a child. Liam was treating her like one even though he was only two years older. Did he want to take care of her? Did he know what that might mean?

She'd spent a week caring for Greg at home before the doctor admitted him into ICU. Then, she'd spent another week caring for Audrey before the doctor had also admitted her to the ICU. Life had become snippets of time she didn't remember filling, time she'd spent peering through hospital windows, masked, trembling. Within a month, they were both gone. Her family—gone.

The road wound out of the forest and into a long green valley, with hills piled beside it. Houses perched here and there on the hillsides; horses and cattle grazed in fenced fields. Liam turned the car into a gravel driveway and drove up to a house.

The tiny curtained window at the top of the two-story house probably opened into an attic filled with discarded items. Throwaways, like her.

Why had she never visited Liam here? Why had she and Greg and Audrey never come?

The sun burst out from behind the massive gray storm cloud. She shaded her eyes with one hand and clutched the camera bag with the other. The car stopped. Her pictures fell into the seat as she opened the door.

Liam bent to retrieve them. "Nice pictures. Didn't remember you being a photographer. And a good one."

"They're Audrey's pictures. She took a photography class last semester in college."

"This is an interesting one. Looks like laundry, flying in the sky." A wide grin erupted on his face.

Samantha glanced at her brother as he ducked and emerged from the car. There was no point in telling him the story she'd invented about the picture. She'd wanted the photo to mean something, wanted to know why Audrey had snapped the shot.

In her mind, Audrey took the photo the day before Greg showed symptoms. Laundry day. There'd been rain. Lightning. Thunder. No electricity. She'd hung the laundry in the house, bedsheets and underwear, linens. Problem solved.

She turned away from the car.

A smiling woman stepped down from the porch and opened her arms. Kate must expect a hug, but Samantha couldn't do it. Her heavy arms and legs drug her down, consumed every ounce of energy as she struggled to walk. Unshed tears threatened to burst the skin holding the tears inside her. One foot in front of the other. Keep moving. She remained dry-eyed.

She stared at the sky-blue house as she walked toward the porch, carefully stepping around puddles that dotted the yard from the earlier storm. Behind her, Liam whispered to Kate, "Hardly a word since the airport."

Samantha struggled up the porch steps, gripping the handrail, and waited for Liam to open the door.

Her own house was brown brick, with wide, low windows and eaves covering the deep porch. Her house was long rooms and painted ceilings. Echoes and looming memories filled her house. She couldn't be there.

Liam stepped up beside her. "Here you go. Come inside and have a look." He pushed the wide blue door open and Samantha stepped into the front hallway. Her mouth gaped.

Shirts on hangers hung from the light fixtures. Bedsheets draped the bookcases. Pictures on the wall beside the staircase served as hooks to hold more hangers, with white shirts, white coveralls, white tablecloths, white napkins, white dresses. A breeze poured in through open windows on all sides of the house.

White shapes fluttered.

Bright light shimmered.

She imagined a smiling face peeking from behind the white sheets. Audrey? Her mind snapped a picture.

A chorus of voices called. Dazed, she peered into the living room. Nieces and nephews, a grand or two. Family.

She wasn't alone.

A single tear traveled down her cheek. And then another, and another until a river of white-hot tears streamed from her eyes.

The dam inside her broke.

MARY COLEY

Mary Coley, an Oklahoma native, is the author of seven mysteries and numerous short stories. She has been a member of Tulsa NightWriters and the Oklahoma Writers Federation, Inc., since 2002. Twice a finalist in the Oklahoma Book Awards, Coley was honored to receive the Hillerman Award from New Mexico/Arizona Book Awards in 2018 for her mystery, *Blood on the Cimarron*. She and her husband Daryl live in Jenks.

The Great Storm

by **Cayden Henderson**

1

The dark unending abyss swallowed me, eating its way through my consciousness and decaying the thin covering of my soul until driving me to the far-left sides of hell. Trying to fight through the branches of darkness felt useless, as the viral infection throbbed and grew deeper like a fungus. I felt the pulsing fatal monstrosity in my feverish, trembling head. Infection was slowly making my left side numb, as well as blinding the vision I have had for the past 30 years. The road was hard to walk on. My final stance was present, then I stumbled to the ground.

I used my good arm to crawl my way off the rough gravel. Rocks tore my fingernails, making them raw, bleeding, and sore. But, of course, that wasn't too rough of a deal, considering I was almost hit by a passing vehicle going 100 mph, before I tumbled down into a dark green swampy mess of a ditch. I struggled to raise up.

My blurry vision slowly focused on a gleaming tower of wood and brick, menacing upon my eyes, with the lights of hell shining through the rough panels of shiny glass. After an hour or so, too weak to walk, I crawled to the front door.

2

A solid fifteen knocks before my greeting. My knuckles broke because of the repeated punching at the door. As the door opened, I could see it all. Smooth reddish wood floors. Coffee cream walls. A blue sofa that you could imagine melting your ass into before watching the glorious television in front of it. A kitchen, with warm jade-colored tiles, emitting the overwhelming aroma of fresh hazelnut coffee.

All of these visions in the background captured my attention before I noticed the hairy legs of this man. His feet were wrapped with velvet slippers. I looked up with envy, embarrassed as he gazed upon my mangled, soon-to-be corpse. He was not surprised by my request, nor my appearance. I guess you could say the introduction with this figure was short, and simple.

"I need in. Just for a while. I won't be long," I said with an urgent tone.

"Why should I let a filthy, bleeding troll into my house, only to rot on my couch?"

I suppose he did have a point. Who would? Real life isn't like a horror movie where someone might let anyone in their house if they were in trouble. I spoke.

"If you shut your door on me, then I will rot on your porch. Suppose the police stroll by tomorrow and find my dead body on your property, all mangled. We both know that wouldn't work out particularly well for you."

The man looked around, before dragging me to the blue sofa, where I would collapse.

3

"So, what is it? What do you want with me?" the man said.

"Well, let's start with names. We'll get to the rest in a minute."

"Sure, I guess that makes sense. Anything to get you out of my house."

"I will have you know that my name is George. Just George. Nothing else. I write for the newspaper." I looked at my blood dripping on his blue sofa. "Do you have any bandages?"

"Yes. I do. Let me get you some." The man went up the stairs of his large house, only to walk, what seemed to me, down a hallway. I could tell this from the way he walked in a straight motion to the left side of the house. The man returned down the stairs.

"Here, hold pressure on your wound." He handed me a gauze pad. "My name's Stark by the way. I'm a medical student, down at the university, toward Maple Street."

"You don't look like a medical student."

"Why do you say that?"

"I don't know. It just seems it. What's your area of medicine?"

"I plan to specialize in neurosurgery. But it seems you're about to die, and the look on your face tells me you're probably wondering about the smell from my basement. I wouldn't let anyone pass with a mystery eating on them, so I'll tell you right out. I have dead bodies down there."

"Dead bodies?" What sort of madman resides with dead bodies in the basement? "What do you do with them?" I ventured.

"I'm practicing reanimation. In fact, this may alarm you, but now that you're here I will use your body after you die. Whether you like it or not. You can't get out of here if you tried."

"You wouldn't dare," I rasped, quelling a nagging cough.

"Oh, I think I would."

"You're a preposterous man!"

"Say what you will. You're the one who's going to be at the wrong end of an electric saw by the end of the night. Dead or not."

Dismayed, I watched Stark fetch coffee. He returned and set down two steaming mugs on his coffee table, seemingly awaiting the story of my infection.

4

It was 11:00 pm at the end of my shift, on a Sunday. A night at the news station can be exhilarating. Especially when I am assigned to write on a suspicious subject that has something to do with violence, and a possible connection to the government. Feeling miserable, I walked towards the back of the building, the street lights getting smaller and smaller, engulfing me in the dark. As the concrete curb turned round, I noticed my car missing. Was it stolen? Or towed? I took a halting breath. Now, I would have to walk back to my apartment.

After an hour or so of walking, I was almost to the complex. Strength wavering, I stopped at a convenience store near the apartment and paid for an energy drink and spicy chips. I ate all of it outside, then spotted a homeless man on the corner. A vague sense of recollection swept over my head like seeing an old friend. But know this man, I did not. Getting closer I began not to see him. His features seemed to lose themselves in darkness.

The man's vagueness crept further into my mind, as I struggled to get hold of an image of him. He turned his head to me. To my horror, what was seen, was unexplainable. The features of his face were gone. Not that he didn't have a face, but what was there, was simply not. Who was this stranger?

What was made in my mind, ultimately left, as he stood. Shorter than I imagined, but taller than I thought. The lights of the convenience store dimmed, and the outsider seemed to blend within it. With the lights gone, I could feel a shiver down my spine. Space began to lighten, and I, as well as the figure, appeared. Even though I could see him, he was indescribable. He spoke, but not with his mouth.

I could not hear his voice. No, I could feel it, as if soundwaves attached themselves directly to my cerebral cortex, not coming in through my ears. No, he did not say anything, but he implied speech, without sound. A subliminal message if you will, but without a surface. Grasps of knowledge were all I needed. Yet, I, a human, could not process it all. My mind imploded with this recent knowledge. All sanity was broken now.

There were forces beyond the human race, and beyond them were even more powerful forces. Forces that did not care about us. Forces that only found us an annoyance. Yet, they were not evil, no. They simply thought of us as flies. Yes, we are living creatures, but if we died, they would not care.

Our solar system was a planned creation that failed, and so, they sought to destroy it, in fear for their lives. These forces created the world a short time ago, and to keep us from knowing too much, they set up a fake past, as an explanation of things. Science and our sense of being was mentally ingrained when we were created, to keep us from questioning things by having a simple explanation.

Our solar system was originally meant to keep a solid chain of beings, gradually getting smaller and smaller. Except when our turn came around, they forgot to put in knowledge of worlds smaller than ours. Almost a Catch-22 if you will. If they put in knowledge too hard for our minds to handle, our minds would implode and would not be able to keep the chain going, thus endangering themselves. If they didn't put in the knowledge, the chain would stop, and their lives would still be in peril.

The universe would end either way, so, the only solution to

keep everything rolling was to reverse time by killing off all the species, until the highest power was left and would start over again. Like an endless ping pong game, where no one wins or loses. They sent a virus down that we humans named COVID-19, and only in a matter of time would we soon become extinct.

This strange figure was sent down to blend in and watch how things were going. It just happened that I stumbled upon him. He noticed I was suspicious. As soon as I received this other-worldly information, I could feel myself fainting. Everything got dim. I opened my eyes to a dark street and intense pain. No convenience store nearby. From the pain in my side, it appeared the creature had stabbed me, to keep me from spilling information, I suppose.

5

By the time I ended my story, Stark was glaring at me and growing very irritated. Our coffee was finished.

"If you are scamming me, why would you think I would believe you?" he asked. "And even if you really think that happened, again, how would you expect me to believe you?"

"I don't know. I guess that will be up to you. I know what I said is true in my mind, but you can think whatever you want about me. It doesn't matter anyway." I stifled a cough and gripped my side against the ache that blossomed. "I will be dead in less than two hours."

Stark looked down thoughtfully at his lap. I could see that he had a sudden thought, because he jumped to his feet in an instant, said nothing, headed to the stairs, and walked up with great pounding force. As I sat, I could feel viral parasites eating away at my organs. I managed to crawl over to the counter and took four ibuprofen. Within sight, a wheelchair stood by his basement. My God, have people come before me? Am I some sort of bait?

6

"What are you trying to do to me? Is this all a sham?" I screamed when he returned.

"How dare you insult me in my own house. First you rot on my steps, then out of the decency of my own heart, I let your filthy, mongrel-self stumble in here, and you have the audacity to insult me. How dare you!"

"How come you speak the way you do?" I retorted. "How come you conveniently had pain medication on the counter when I came in? Are you a part of the government? Answer me! Are there others like me? Are you involved with beings from other worlds that unloosed the deadly virus? Am I the bait, since I saw what they do, and what we are and will be? Are you a killer? Answer me! Answer m-"

A clap of thunder raged outside of the house. Stark looked toward his basement frightfully. "It's time. It's time. Ha-ha. It's time."

Stark hurried up the stairs again. If I were to escape, I needed to make my move. I struggled to the wheelchair and rolled down the hallway. Barely scraping by a bedroom, I spied a Ruger Mark IV on the bed. I grabbed it up and checked the clip. Fully loaded. My God, he really has been capturing people in this clean colossal monster of a house. I sensed something behind me and suddenly, a ripping sound. Duct tape. A hand gripped my shoulder.

"You Son of a—"

Stark tried to gag me, stuffing something in my mouth. CRUNCH! A snap down to his knuckle. I spit the cloth out. He got back up and smacked me right in the jaw. It was broken for sure now. Slowly coming out of shock from the hit, I saw him reach for the strip of duct tape. Luckily, I was locked and loaded. BLAM! A shot to the abdomen. POW! A shot to the arm. BOOM! A shot to the leg.

Stark struggled to get up, his right leg wobbling sideways when pressure was put on it. Blood flowed out of his mouth like a waterfall, moistening what once was chapped lips.

"How could you do this?" he rasped. "I let you in! I gave you something to drink! This is how you repay me?"

"You never cared," I said. "The only reason you let me in was so you could keep me as one of your unfortunate test subjects. You are a menace, and I won't let you leave this world without me having something to do with it."

Stark looked grimly behind him at the basement doors, open like the gaping mouth of a monster. I lunged from the wheelchair at him. Our bodies rolled over and over and, finally, tumbled down the stairs. It was evident now that we could both never walk again.

7

My eyes opened. Rotting meat in my nostrils. I looked over. Stark's body lay beside me, gushing blood. Just beyond him, were his human lab rats. All dismembered. In the dim lighting, the putrid smell somehow made the sight worse. A male head in a metal pan. This man's top had been sawed off, revealing slimy, dark-pink, worm-shaped bits of brain. Another body had the skin ripped off. It appeared that he had tried to use the thin tan material to make different styles of clothing. A half-finished vest hung on a hook.

This man was a lunatic, but am I just the same? Was I just hit really hard on the head outside of the convenience store? Was my other worldly encounter just made up in my mind? It can't be, but I don't know. Is my life just a memory of my new life, planted by the aliens? Is my life just a dream? Was this man with the government? Is this all just an illusion? What waits beyond me? Heaven? Hell? Nothing? A Reversal Through Time?

There are so many questions, but none of them can be answered. Here I am now. Down to my final breaths, in a freak's basement full of decaying corpses. I do not know the truth, but all I can do now is pray to God.

8

Outside the house, a storm thundered. A great storm. An end, or not? A great storm. The wind howled. The gutters flooded. Sick people. Just a storm? A great storm. People dead. A storm? A great storm. Hope. Despair. Lunatic, or Sane. Human or Inhuman. The storm brewed and brewed and brewed. But will it end? This Storm. This Great Viral Storm.

CAYDEN HENDERSON

•••

Cayden Henderson is a 14-year-old student at Owasso High School. Though an avid reader of all genre's, he likes science fiction and supernatural horror, with H.P. Lovecraft, Edgar Allan Poe, and Stephen King, as his preferred authors. However, his favorite book is *Catcher in the Rye*, by J.D. Salinger.

A music lover, Cayden plays the saxophone, guitar, banjo, ukulele, kalimba, and, including, on occasion, the Australian didgeridoo. He enjoys listening to Jazz and Punk. His favorite pastime is creating music with a synthesizer and drum machine.

Cayden collects vinyl records, and a wide assortment of movies from his best liked directors, Quentin Tarantino, Martin Scorsese, Stanley Kubrick, and Alfred Hitchcock. Other activities include camping time spent perfecting his skateboarding technique.

The Best of Times

by **Donna Welch Jones**

Kylie wondered what it was like to venture into the real world: sit on a park bench, run down a trail, feel the breeze in her hair, or touch someone's hand.

Tears made crooked paths down the scars on her face. Twelve years ago, a dog mutilated her face. At first, her dad pretended she was normal, but even at six-years-old she knew better. Stares proved that she was pitied, feared, gross— a monster. Too horrible to look at or speak to, much less play with fair-faced children. Dad eventually conceded that she had no place in public.

Seeing Kylie's scarred face every day reminded her mother that she didn't keep her little girl safe. Over the last twelve years, at least once a month, the woman ranted, cried, and apologized. Kylie's perception of herself as a freak was verified by her mother's actions. On her nineteenth birthday, Dad found her an efficiency apartment. He said it was a way to stabilize her mental health—not Kylie's, her mother's.

Kylie's eyes focused on the television screen. A reporter interviewed an angry woman. Her arms flailed. Her stare pierced into the camera lens. "I'm an American. Nobody takes my freedom. I won't be forced to wear a mask—the symbol of tyranny."

"You're my freedom," Kylie told the varicolored masks that lined her coffee table. She selected one and stretched it across her face from ear-to-ear. *Today, April 5, 2020, I will go outside like a normal person.*

Kylie's heart pounded as she released the lock and turned the doorknob. She stepped into the hallway, looked left then right, twirled and rushed back into the apartment. The toilet collected the vomit that spewed from her mouth. She lowered to the rug.

Tomorrow is a better day—less park visitors on Mondays.

The next day, Kylie took a nausea pill an hour before her adventure. Her mantra blurted out as she approached the door, "I can do it, I can do it, I can do it." The lock released. Palm sweat moistened the doorknob as it turned. Outside the door, she waited for the nausea. It didn't come, only a little queasiness.

Perhaps I should wait until tomorrow.

Kylie startled.

The mailman walked forward, "Sorry, I frightened you. I'm delivering a package to your neighbor. Is he home?"

"I don't know him."

He smiled, "Are you going out? It's a beautiful day."

She stared at the floor, "I thought about it."

"Some people are afraid because of COVID-19, but you're young and have a mask. Just stay six feet away from others. Go enjoy the sunshine!"

Kylie nodded and walked toward the stairs. Although the day was cool, sweat trickled down her sides.

Dad drove past a park on the way to her doctor visits, so she knew to turn east at the corner. The breeze cooled the heat invading her body. As she jogged, she observed yellow tulips and purple phlox decorating front yards. The sun washed her in brightness. Her pace quickened when she neared the park, then slowed when she saw two unmasked girls—laughing and coming toward her. They crossed the street when they got closer.

Bile burned in her throat. *Did they see my face?* Kylie felt her mask, it was snug and in place. She forced herself forward. Ten minutes at the park was her goal. She noticed a masked girl sitting alone on a bench.

Kylie sat several feet from the stranger.

The girl pointed, "Look at the baby squirrels playing in the tree. They're so cute."

Kylie watched as the animals ran up the tree, scurried between branches, scampered down the trunk, then chased each other in a circle around the tree.

"I've never seen you here before," she called.

Kylie touched her mask, "I'm not an outside person."

"Because of the virus?"

"No."

"I'm Maria. I like your flowered mask."

"Thanks. I'm Kylie."

A teenage boy yelled, "FREAK" as he crossed the street.

Maria jumped up, "I must leave!"

The guy charged forward and blocked Maria's path. "You're too ugly to be in public."

She whimpered, "I'm going."

He ripped Maria's mask down.

Kylie gasped.

"Your face scared that girl, freak. Get out of here."

Maria ran. Kylie chased after her, listening for the bully's footsteps behind them—none.

Maria glanced over her shoulder, lost footing, and crashed to the sidewalk.

She sat up and yelled, "Go away, I don't want your pity."

Kylie pulled a tissue from her purse. "Your knee is bleeding."

"Get away from me. I don't want your help. I saw the look on your face when that cruel guy pulled my mask down. I heard you gasp."

Kylie knelt beside her. Her hand trembled when she pulled down her own mask.

Maria stammered, "What happened to your face?"

"A close encounter with an angry dog. You?"

"Nasal cavity cancer. I knew better than to come out, usually the mask keeps me safe from strangers. It's my former friends who harass me."

"Do you know that jerk?"

"He was my senior prom date last year—when I was pretty. My former classmates tease him about dating a creepy faced girl. That's why he's so angry—like the cancer was my fault."

Kylie pressed the tissue against the gash. "The masks are the only reason I *can* go out. I pretend that I'm a normal person." She winced, "My freedom will end with the virus."

Maria murmured, "Mine, too."

Uncertainty snuck into Kylie's voice. "Do you want to watch a movie? My apartment is close, and I have Pepsi and popcorn."

"I'd like that. I'll phone Mom and tell her that I'm spending the afternoon with a friend."

Kylie turned away. Tears filled her eyes— *a friend*!

DONNA WELCH JONES

•••

Donna is the author of *Unbreak Their Hearts*, *Beautiful Bait,* and the *Sheriff Lexie Wolfe Mysteries*. She has won awards in the Writer's Digest National Writing Competition. She is a member of the Oklahoma Writers' Federation, Tulsa NightWriters, and Mystery Writers of America.

Like Iris in a Ravine

by **J.A. Kimmel**

The new coronavirus had been an official pandemic for eight weeks. I couldn't go to lunch with a friend, work out at the gym, or have my hair done. Some people—like my twenty-year-old daughter, Kayleigh—went out anyway, in spite of this respiratory disease called COVID-19. But, except for runs to the grocery store to scope out whatever the panic-buyers left behind, I remained at home.

At least I could walk my cockapoo, Jack, around the neighborhood without wearing a mask or washing my hands with sanitizer. Thank goodness my boyfriend and I lived in a small lakeside town surrounded by farms, instead of in a metropolis with a higher death toll.

A tug on the leash in my hand jerked me forward. I smiled at the way Jack's nose zig-zagged across the ground, his blonde fur shining.

"Whaddaya smell, lovey-boy?"

Jack wagged his tail, and a breeze brushed against my face, bringing with it the scent of green things growing.

We'd covered half a mile of our daily route without seeing a soul, without smelling the gaseous fumes of lawnmowers, without hearing the whir of tires on asphalt or the rumble of jets overhead. Front doors were stuck shut, cars vegged in driveways, and flowering weeds bubbled from lawns like colored springs.

The silence sunk deep into my core, releasing a vise I hadn't known was there, and my shoulders relaxed. Birdsong and Jack's steady pant tickled my ears.

Ahead lay an island flowerbed as multihued as a painter's palette. Dozens of ruffled blooms rose on long stems above sword-like leaves. Iris, the bearded variety. They greeted me like old friends.

I stopped beside the bed, remembering my grandparents' iris. As a child, I ran barefoot toward the flags of color lining their garden fence for the simple joy of burrowing my nose into the flowers' soft centers. I'd close my eyes and breathe-in their sweet fragrances. Orange blossom. Spice. Chocolate.

Before Kayleigh's birth, I planted bearded iris in our garden so she, too, could play among them. When she held a bloom against her nose and took a deep breath, the large petals clung to her face like a hug. Then, oh, how she'd giggle!

No longer did I run barefoot anywhere; I wore orthotic shoes. My grandparents had passed, and I rarely saw Kayleigh. She lived an hour and a half away. But nothing could dull the pleasure of a bearded iris's scent, not even a virus.

Bending over a blue-purple one, I inhaled and smiled. Grape soda.

I took a picture of the iris bed with my phone and sent it to Kayleigh, along with a text message.

Wish you could smell these. Whatcha doin'?

Ding! My phone's screen lit up.

Kayleigh.

What's a headache called that hurts when you stand up for, like, five seconds and then stops?

Like a head rush or like the ones you've been having?

Neither. It almost brings me to my knees. My whole body hurts.

Warning bells clanged in my mind. Since she'd been on her own, Kayleigh had enlisted Google's aid in treating herself for many ailments, including bladder infections and the flu, not to mention hangovers. This time, she wasn't self-diagnosing.

Head and body aches can be coronavirus symptoms. Do you have fever?

Yeah, but I don't have the f---ing coronavirus.

I visualized her rolled eyes. *How do you know you haven't caught it from your friends? You live in Tulsa, in an apartment. Crowded conditions increase the risk factor.*

My friends aren't sick. The city lifted quarantine.

Your friends could be asymptomatic carriers. The city is only entering Phase I of a gradual reopening. Not meant to be a party.

Are you going to start going out?

Ray and I are high-risk. No point in tempting fate, which is why you should go to doctor.

I'm literally fine now. I got a pet sitting job I can walk to.

Typical tactic—change the subject. *Great! Where?*

When she didn't reply, I texted, *Take disinfecting wipes with you. Go to doctor if symptoms reappear. Please!*

Thirty minutes later, Jack and I returned home through the open garage door.

Smoke pervaded the four-car space and office niche. Two cars and a bass boat rested below a wall-mounted television. With a cigarette dangling from his mouth, my boyfriend, Ray, sat at his desk, playing E6Golf on his iPad and watching the news.

"The number of coronavirus cases in the United States has now surpassed one million," an anchorman stated.

And there was no sure cure.

"Today, Virginia had its first coronavirus-related death, bringing the total deaths in the U.S. to 65,646."

Virginia. My ex and I spent three weeks there, waiting to lawfully bring Kayleigh home, hoping our dream baby's birthmother didn't change her mind about adoption. How tiny Kayleigh had been! Now, at ninety-nine pounds, she was still tiny.

"We're back," I said, removing Jack's leash.

"Already?" Ray replied, sweeping his finger across the iPad's screen.

Frowning at his response, I described Kayleigh's symptoms. "I'm concerned."

"Birdie!" he exclaimed, looking up. "Did you remember to carry your pepper spray?"

Was he even listening? "Yes. I need to go to Tulsa."

Unfortunately, my wheels were at the repair shop and would be for about two weeks. The cars in the garage belonged to Ray.

"Can I drive the Honda?" I asked.

"Why?"

"To make sure Kayleigh sees a doctor."

"She don't need you for that. Do you realize how much gas would cost, plus wear and tear on the car? Them tires is already wore out from all my trips to try and get that Tulsa warehouse remodeled."

"You know she doesn't have a car."

"She would if she hadn't wrecked the one your dad give her. It's her own fault she never got it out of the tow yard. She can find a ride."

I heaved a sigh. This conversation wasn't going anywhere, and apparently, neither was I.

"You might be right," I said, glancing at the clock. "Time to start dinner."

When our meal was ready, I called Ray in. After I gave thanks, we ate in silence.

Ray had been in the garage all day. With the exception of my walk, I'd spent the day in my workroom, handcrafting a door wreath for one of my Etsy customers. Shouldn't partners at least talk to one another?

"You haven't mentioned your son lately," I ventured.

Ray shrugged. "Haven't heard from Shawn since the last time he wanted rent money."

"Is—"

"You think Kayleigh's really sick?"

"Yeah, I do. She's been sick a lot lately, but she won't go to the doctor. The only thing I know to do is put her in the car and take her myself."

"She's prob'ly broke 'cause she blew her money on pot, and she's too lazy to get a full-time job."

"Before the pandemic, she said she was looking."

Ray's voice became strident. "When are you gonna quit bein' so gullible? She lies about ever'thing. Look how she lied to your parents about goin' to class after they give her money for college. I don't blame 'em for bein' done with her."

"Some kids are late bloomers. I was."

"Look how many times she's lied to you. You raised her the best you could, but she's not like you. She's not your blood. You oughta be done with her, like her father is."

I drew myself up. "Kayleigh is my daughter in every way that counts. She's young, and she's always been less mature than her peers. I still have hope. She said she found a pet sitting job."

"That's prob'ly a lie, too."

"Could be," I said, ready to end the conversation.

Over the next two days, I spent most of my time designing wreaths, but I made sure Jack got his "walkies."

Thursday, around two o' clock, we set out, with Jack yipping in his sing-song way and tugging so hard on the leash that I had to hold it with both hands. I knew how he felt, and so, we ran.

We ran until we reached the iris bed. Out of breath, I slowed to a walk.

The iris stood tall, their faces glowing with color. Lemon-yellow. Tangerine-pink. Wisteria blue. Plum red. They took me back to the time I discovered iris petals scattered throughout the house like confetti and followed the trail. It led to my five-year-old's bedroom.

Dismayed, I asked, "Kayleigh Anne, *why* did you tear up Mommy's iris?"

She grinned. "*You* know, Mommy." Leaning closer, she whispered, "I'm practicing."

Realization dawned. "Because *you* are going to be a flower girl!" I swung her around.

"For Lisa's wedding!" she exclaimed, laughing.

My iris plants looked like headless scarecrows, but they blossomed again the following spring. That was the thing about iris. They were so forgiving that they'd grow almost anywhere, and they multiplied, providing greater beauty every year.

When the bearded iris in my grandparents' garden began crowding one another, my grandmother would dig up the clumps and divide the rhizomes, discarding any with rot or insect holes. She'd toss the damaged rhizomes into a tree-lined ravine near the house and replant the healthy ones.

One spring, while playing, I wandered to the ravine's edge and peered down. At the bottom, a creek trickled between steep banks dappled with shade. There, amid tree roots, broken limbs, and tall grass, a rainbow of long-necked iris strained to catch the sunlight. Hundreds of blossoms perfumed the air. Left to fend for themselves, they hadn't merely survived; they'd rallied.

When Jack and I returned home, I read my mail.

Ding!

Kayleigh.

My entire body hurts, again, like I've been running for days. So much pain, Mom. Even my fingers. I just barfed.

I called her.

She answered on the first ring.

"Kayleigh, honey, you've got to go to the doctor immediately. Something is terribly wrong."

"I know, but I can't afford it."

"Call your doctor's office and ask if you can work out a payment plan. I'll help with the cost. Then let me know what they say."

"They won't do it because I owe them money." Her voice quavered. "I feel like I'm gonna die, Momma."

"You'll have to go to the Emergency Room. Can one of your friends take you?"

"The other day, Zach said he would, but I want my momma."

"I want my girl, too, but I'm not there, baby. Call Zach and have him take you to the ER."

She didn't respond.

"Kayleigh . . . Kayleigh,"—my voice grew louder—"are you still there?"

"Yeah," she murmured. "Wanna sleep."

Alarm snaked up my spine. "What have you taken?"

"Tylenol and aspirin."

"How much?"

"I dunno," she mumbled as our call disconnected.

I called her back.

No answer.

Are you going to the ER? I texted, my heart racing.

I'll try.

When?

When Zach gets off work.

When will that be?

While waiting for her response, I rushed to the garage, phone in hand. "Ray, Kayleigh needs to go to the ER, and I need to be with her."

"She's goin' to the ER?" he exclaimed, looking up from his iPad and lighting a cigarette. "Do you know how much that's gonna cost? She only wants you to pay for it. She's just like Shawn. You gotta quit enablin' her."

Hot tears pooled in my eyes. "This is different."

"Call your parents. They live two miles from her."

I stared at him, shaking my head. In their eighties, with preexisting conditions, my parents were high-risk.

"Yeah, you're right. They'd prob'ly think you wanted *them* to pay for it."

Was money all he cared about? "I *have* to go to Tulsa. I'm all she's got."

"Whose fault is that?"

"It's—"

"What are you gonna do there, anyway?"

Didn't he *know*? Thinking out loud, I said, "I can probably get there before Zach gets off work . . . and her dog will need to be walked."

"If you go in her nasty apartment, you'll pick up fleas. Then you'll bring 'em back here to Jack."

For a moment, I hesitated. Then, I whirled around to go back inside.

"Where are you goin'?"

"To pack," I said. "Fleas can be treated."

"You're not goin', and that's final!" he yelled.

I spun to face him, setting my jaw. How dare he tell me that I couldn't help my own daughter!

"Haven't you been listenin' to the f---in' news?" he shouted.

"How can I help but listen to the news when you keep that accursed TV on all day?" I shouted back.

His eyes widened, but he continued at the same volume. "They're not gonna let you in the hospital with her. You'll just have to drop her off. And what if she has COVID? You'll catch it, too!" He ran his hands through his hair.

The words I'd been about to hurl at him froze and shattered in my mind. He was right.

Placing his palms on the kitchen counter, Ray lowered his voice. "Don't you understand? You *can't* help her this time." With that, he turned and shoved open the door to the garage.

It swung closed behind him like a slap in my face.

I'd known that hospitals were prohibiting visitors for adult patients in order to minimize the virus's spread. But in my fervor, I'd forgotten that my child was now an adult. I was as "nonessential" as the businesses ordered to close by the governor. Was I really supposed to do *nothing*?

For the next four hours, like a hamster in an aquarium, I kept the wheel spinning. I cooked and cleaned, periodically calling or texting Kayleigh.

No response.

Was she lying unconscious on the floor, or was Zach speeding her to the hospital?

You okay? I texted, again, at 7:32 p.m., jumping when my phone rang a few seconds later.

"I'm at the hospital," Kayleigh murmured.

I breathed a sigh of relief. Tears welled in my eyes. "Thank Zach for me."

"Okay. They're keeping me overnight. I have some kind of infection."

"Have they tested you for COVID?"

"I don't remember."

"What drugs have they given you?"

"Fentanyl and Ibuprofen."

An opioid. "No wonder you sound woozy. My poor baby."

"Do I need to come and take care of Odin?"

"No, Hakeem's gonna feed and walk him. Mom, it hurts too much to talk."

And I was quizzing her.

After we said our goodbyes, I sat down at my worktable, consoling myself with the thought that Kayleigh was where she needed to be.

Another four hours dragged by before I heard from her again.

They tested me for COVID. Shoved a big honking Q-tip into my brain.

Next, a picture of Kayleigh's wrist with a yellow band around it popped up. The band said *fall* in bold black letters.

I'm a fall risk. LOL!

Laughter. That was positive. A former gymnast, Kayleigh took pride in her coordination.

As soon as I woke the next morning, I called her. The hospital staff had run a variety of diagnostics, but the doctors still weren't sure what was wrong. She'd been put on the COVID floor in case she tested positive. That way, she'd already be quarantined.

COVID floor? What if she caught the virus while waiting for test results?

When we hung up, I stared out the window at the lake. Kayleigh could die. And I wouldn't be there to hold her hand. Who'd make sure she was well cared for? Wouldn't dying of COVID be like drowning? I pictured myself sinking beneath the lake's surface, its wetness sealing me off from the outside world. Holding my breath, I imagined water filling my lungs. When they were about to burst, I expelled the pent-up air with a cry, gasping for breath.

That evening, while I was flipping hamburger patties, the door from the garage banged open, and Ray hurried in.

Startled, I dropped the spatula.

"Why are you so jumpy?" he asked, tugging at his belt as he beelined to the bathroom.

Ding!

No COVID! Kayleigh's message read.

Snatching my phone off the counter, I called her.

"Yea!" I exclaimed when she answered. "So, what do they think is wrong?"

"I don't know," she said faintly.

"Any idea when you'll see a doctor again?"

"Nope. Mom, I promise I'll text when I have more info, but until then, I really need to sleep because, every time I wake up, I'm literally in a lot of pain."

I wasn't helping.

We said our I-love-you-goodbye's as Ray returned to the kitchen.

"Who was that?" he asked.

"Kayleigh. Her COVID test was negative!"

"Oh. That's good," he said. "When are they dischargin' her?"

"They're not. They still don't know what's wrong."

He frowned, drawing his brows together. "How long's she been there?"

"Two—"

"She can't afford that. Did she tell 'em she don't have no health insurance?"

"Y—"

"Since they tested her for COVID, maybe the gover'ment'll pick up the tab, or maybe they'll just write it off when she don't pay her bill. *You* can't afford to pay it. You make peanuts." He shook his head. "And *I* aint payin' it. I dunno." Throwing his hands in the air, he strode back into the garage.

After dinner, I took Jack on his walkie.

By the time I remembered to stop and smell the iris, we'd already passed them. I trudged on, staring at the weather-beaten asphalt directly in front of me. When I finally looked up, Jack and I were turning into our driveway. My faithful lovey-boy had guided me home.

As we entered the garage, the television pelleted me with the evening news. "Oklahoma has reported its sixth death from COVID-19."

Always death. What about the survivors?

I was removing Jack's leash when Kayleigh called.

"They're keeping me over the weekend," she said. "Hold on. Dina's in here. I'm gonna put you on the speakerphone."

"Who's Dina?"

"My nurse."

"Who is it?" asked Ray, a cigarette bobbing between his lips.

"Kayleigh," I mouthed.

"Put her on the speaker," he said.

Nodding, I turned it on.

"They diagnosed me with a urinary tract infection," Kayleigh continued. The doctor said if I'd waited another twenty-four hours to check in, I'd have gone into a coma."

I sucked in a breath.

"You're shittin' me!" exclaimed Ray.

"It's true," said Dina. "The infection turned septic, but she's gonna be all right."

"Thank you for all you've done," I said.

"My pleasure," Dina replied. "Kayleigh's everybody's favorite patient."

A lump formed in my throat. I'd been a stay-at-home mom since Kayleigh's birth. I'd witnessed every developmental milestone and wiped away every tear. I'd never even hired a babysitter. This was the most serious illness of Kayleigh's life, but I wasn't there. Strangers were taking care of my daughter.

That night, on his way to bed, Ray poked his head into my workroom. "I gotta go to Tulsa to pay the contractor sometime soon. You can go with me and, maybe, see Kayleigh."

Relief flooded my body. "I'd like to pick her up from the

hospital. She's going to be weak."

"When's she gettin' out?"

"She doesn't know."

"I dunno when he's gonna be finished. Maybe Tuesday," he said, walking away.

The instant my eyes opened on Sunday morning, I pulled up my text messages and received two precious gifts.

Happy Mother's Day to literally the best mom on the planet! I get to go home today!

My heart leapt. Ray and I could probably get to Tulsa in time to pick up Kayleigh. But would he agree to that?

I called her. She didn't have a ride, so I explained my situation and said I'd ask Ray if we could leave two days early.

"No, don't," she said. "I can manage."

I choked back a sob. "I'm—"

"It's okay, Momma. I understand. I literally have no idea what time they'll release me, anyway."

After we said goodbye, a dam burst inside of me, and I wept.

Just before noon, my phone dinged.

Kayleigh.

Lookie here! A picture of a tree-lined street, taken through a car window, followed her text.

Woo-hoo! Freedom! I texted back. *Who's taking you home?*

Guilt washed over me when I read her response.

Uber. Don't worry. The driver is wearing a mask.

Good.

A mask. Before the pandemic, that statement would have frightened me.

Tuesday morning, I awakened to a furry head nuzzling my cheek. "We're going to see Kayleigh today!" I said, kissing Jack on the nose.

So many people had lost their livelihoods, their homes, their health, and their loved ones owing to COVID-19, but I had not. Like iris in a ravine, we were all doing our best to survive with what we'd been given. In spite of everything, I was blessed.

"Thank you," I whispered.

Then, I took Jack outside.

Lifting my face to catch the sunlight, I closed my eyes and breathed-in the scent of green things growing.

J.A. KIMMEL

A freelance editor, J. A. Kimmel (aka Julie Kimmel-Harbaugh) is also an award-winning writer and a certified educator. Her published works include songs, lesson plans, articles, and short stories. Julie served as Communications Director and Editor of Tulsa NightWriters Club for four years. She is a three-time recipient of the club's Golden Circle award, and in 2015, the membership honored her with the NightWriter of the Year award. Originally from Texas, she now lives on Grand Lake o' the Cherokees in the foothills of the Ozark Mountains.

Seeds of Change

——◆●◆——

by **Renee' La Viness**

~ 2020 ~

"What are these seeds for?" Sasha asked. "Did you order them?"

"I can't even seem to plant a baby," Rance said. "Why would I try planting anything else?"

Sasha slapped him on the shoulder. "We've only been trying for three months. Give us a chance."

"Chance. I like that for a name. It rhymes with Rance. I can hear the neighbors now...

Across the room, Sasha saw Rance.
He didn't seem like much at first glance.
But with a kiss, a ring, and a little romance,
They gave each other a Chance."

"Aww, that is so sweet. And I think that's a perfect name for our first son." Sasha kissed her husband and squeezed his hand.

Rance redirected. "What kind of seeds?"

"I don't know. They were shipped from China. Did you order something from there? Maybe it was part of a special deal someone was offering."

"Hmmm... I don't remember any special deals."

Sasha stared at the clear bag filled with unidentified seeds. "Maybe they made a mistake and sent these instead of what we ordered. What did you order?"

"I didn't order anything. Did you order something?"

"Not that I recall."

Rance looked at the wall clock. "I have to leave for work."

"Did you remember your facemasks?"

"I bought a box of disposables. I'm so tired of all this COVID-19 stuff. I'll be glad when they find a cure or a vaccine."

"Me, too." Sasha set the seed packet on the counter. "I'll try to contact the company later."

"Good idea." Rance gave her a kiss. "I'll see you in a few hours."

~ 2021 ~

Rance put the bowl of oatmeal in the microwave then returned to his task of clearing the clutter on his desk.

"Your breakfast is in the microwave, honey. I'm back in the office."

Sasha stopped at the doorway on her way through. "Thanks. I'm extra hungry this morning."

Rance kissed his wife. "Sorry I didn't bring it to you. I'm trying to get this mess cleaned up before I head to work."

"I know. I'm just sorry I'm feeling so poorly with this pregnancy. It should be over in a couple of months. I'll be glad to be back to the old me and have time to do things I enjoy again."

"And I'll be glad for both of us. Everyone at work keeps saying we'll never sleep after the baby is born. I just laugh. They don't know how much sleep we're missing now."

Sasha turned and waddled toward the kitchen.

Finding a brown envelope with a bag of seeds inside, Rance pulled it out of the tray. "Sasha, is this the seed packet that came in the mail last year? Why do we still have it?"

Sasha yelled from the kitchen, "There was no contact information on it. I heard something, back then, about other people receiving unmarked seed packets from China. I got a little worried about planting them, but I couldn't seem to talk myself into throwing them away. That was back when this COVID-19 stuff first started up."

Rance put the package back in the tray. "I wonder if they ever figured out anything about the seeds. Maybe we should plant them and see what grows."

"Maybe after I have the baby. I'm not up to tending a garden right now."

~ 2023 ~

Sasha pointed. "It's your turn, Neeta."

"Oh, okay." Neeta studied her cards. "Mary, do you have any

fours?"

"Go fish!"

"I thought you had some a while ago," Neeta said.

"I did have one until London took it from me."

Neeta smirked at Mary. "Oh, thanks. Now she knows I have one, too."

Chance ran toward Sasha with a wet diaper hanging a little low on his body. He reached up to the table and handed his mother a clear bag. "Eat?"

"No, no." Sasha took the bag from her son. "These aren't to eat."

"Are those seeds?" London asked. "What kind?"

"I don't know. They came one day in the mail and didn't have a label on them."

"Oooh," Neeta squealed. "Are they some of the seeds China sent over here before everyone died off from the pandemic?"

"Yes," Sasha said.

"Why didn't you plant them?"

"Back then, the government discouraged people from planting them, so Rance and I decided to wait."

Taking the seeds from her friend, Neeta examined them. "They look like pumpkin seeds. You could have your own pumpkin patch and make homemade pumpkin pie! I'd come over for some."

Sasha retrieved the seed packet from her friend and set it on the counter. "Maybe next year. It's too late to plant them now." She quickly changed Chance's diaper and set him in his high chair with some dry cereal to munch on, then returned to the card game.

Mary took a coughing fit, and the girls gathered around to bring her out of it.

Afterward, London patted her on the back and said, "I wish you hadn't got that ugly COVID-19. Between your lungs and my daddy and brother's mud-thick blood, I don't know who is going to die first."

"I'm just glad she's still here with us." Sasha smiled at Mary.

"How many people have died from it?" Neeta asked.

Rance stepped into the room and answered. "Three quarters of Earth's population has died, so far. And what a mess our world is now."

Looking toward Sasha, he asked, "Did you see the Huffines'

home up the road? It looks like some bandits moved in last night."

"More squatters?" London asked.

"Yep," Rance said. "The banks can't seem to secure all the vacant homes before they get vandalized by creeps like that."

Sasha pointed her husband to the next room. "Get out of here and let us finish our game. It's my turn."

~ November, 2025 ~

Rance raked some new weeds out of the garden. "I'm glad you finally planted those seeds, Sasha. Otherwise, I was going to throw them away and hope you'd forgotten about them."

"You know, Rance, I feel so much better than I have in the past couple of years. I wonder if it's just because I've been working in the garden."

Rance leaned over a tomato cage and kissed his wife on the cheek.

London ran across the alley that separated their back yards and rushed to the garden at the side of Sasha's house.

"Sasha! He's cured! My little brother is cured!"

Careful not to step on any plants, Sasha made her way from the garden to her friend. "What are you squawking about, London?"

"Rome is cured!" London jumped up and down, finally grabbing and swinging Sasha in a circle.

"How do you know?"

"The doctor said so."

"But how did it happen? He's had it for a few years with no change. Why now?"

London slowed to a halt and caught her breath. "I don't know why now. But the doc said his blood is flowing freely again. He said other people are starting to show signs of cure, and Dad is looking better, so maybe his next doc appointment will be good, too."

~ January, 2026 ~

[TV BROADCAST] "...Who knows what caused so many people to plant the seeds after such a long time? Too bad it wasn't allowed back in 2020, before eighty-five percent of the population was lost. If only we'd known the Chinese were sharing the cure to the deadly sickness they'd accidentally created..."

The Cough and the Sneeze

by **Renee' La Viness**

Sung to the tune of "The Birds and The Bees"

Let me tell you 'bout the cough and the sneeze
And the fever and the wheeze,
And the quarantine fuss:
It's Coronavirus.

Let me tell you 'bout the mask on my face,
And about social space,
Wash your hands—don't touch your face,
Follow local mandates.

As I look into your frightened eyes,
'Cause that's all that I can see,
I know it's time you learn how the virus spreads
Before you give it to me.

Let me tell you 'bout the cough and the sneeze
And the fever and the wheeze,
And the quarantine fuss:
It's Coronavirus.

Let me tell you 'bout the cough and the sneeze
And the fever and the wheeze,
And the cough and the sneeze,
And the fever and the wheeze…

RENEE' LA VINESS

At thirteen years old, Renee' wrote and performed her own ventriloquism skits. Since then, she has been published in books, magazines, newspapers, and anthologies. From 2013 to 2018, she held an editor position at 4RV Publishing, including two years as the first Children's Corner Imprint Editor. She is the founder/organizer of the annual Meet the Publishers! event in Tulsa, Oklahoma, and a co-founder, organizer of the Read.Write.Share. Conference in Little Rock, Arkansas. She is also an editor, a sponsor/judge for writing contests, and a speaker at writing events.

In her daily life, Renee' is a dedicated volunteer at the local school library and loves reading to elementary school students. She lives in Oklahoma with her writing husband Gene, a bossy "senior citizen" Welsh Corgi, and three ornery chickens.

2020: The Challenge of a Lifetime

by **Xaundra La Viness**

The year 2020 marked a new decade, a promise for more challenges.

COVID-19 was a deadly disease that swept through the villages.

When the new year had first begun,

No one knew our lives would become undone.

Schools were empty, nobody there.

After that, school was taught anywhere.

Homes were filled with schoolwork and cooped-up children.

Scientists worked hard to stop the unseen villain.

As life in quarantine grows really long,

Families struggle to get along.

COVID-19 brought us together.

Let's hope, though, it doesn't last forever.

XAUNDRA LA VINESS

At the ripe old age of one year old, Xaundra La Viness held a daily meeting with all her stuffed animal friends. Every afternoon, they waited patiently for her to climb into their drawer and read a handful of books that swept them away to a fantasy land of fun and excitement. And so began her love of words.

The writing bug bit early, as Xaundra was published twice in elementary school. She attends writers' conferences to learn more and enters contests to practice her skills. In ninth grade, she won a school-wide poetry contest. In 2020, she won First Place in the Youth Poetry Contest at the Arkansas Writers Conference.

Xaundra is talented in other areas, too. At three years old, she designed her first custom pool cue, and at four years old, she was designing beautiful custom jewelry.

As the middle child in a mixed set of six, she is the youngest sibling in one family and the oldest in the other.

Xaundra enjoys reading, singing, dancing, sleeping, helping others (especially animals), sewing, cooking, crafts, working with hair, painting, and as an eco-activist, she is focused on protecting and preserving our planet for future generations.

Bunkhouse Epidemic

by **Jim Laughter**

anch hand Toy Pickett sat on the edge of his cot in the rough-hewn bunkhouse on the Marshall ranch in the western Oklahoma Territory panhandle. His weatherworn saddle lay abandoned in the northwest corner surrounded by his winter coat, bags, and bedroll. His old leather boots stood lonely vigil at the foot of his bunk, while his spurs dangled on a peg driven into an oak post supporting the center beam holding up the sod roof. It rained last night, so a puddle of muddy water pooled on the bare, hardwood plank floor. He wondered why his woolen socks felt damp. He must have trodden through the puddle on his way to piss out the window before daybreak this morning. He hadn't felt like challenging the slippery trail to the outhouse in the dark.

A dozen other cowboys lay scattered around the bunkhouse, either in their bunks or sprawled out on the floor, leaned up against their gear like they did while sleeping out on the Oklahoma prairie. Most were stripped down to their long-johns, covered by their saddle blankets or winter coats to stave off the morning chill. They'd stir out of their bunks soon or foreman Pug Juneau, a transplanted Frenchman from New Orleans, would bust a gut cussing a blue streak at them before sending them out to round up the spring calves and yearling stock. Today was branding day, which means every new steer on the place had to be scorched with Mr. Calvin Marshall's Double-Deuce before the drive to market next week.

Toy pushed up from his bunk to stretch a kink from his back. He stumbled and lurched forward, catching himself on the center post, jangling his spurs. A couple other cowboys stirred at the noise. Someone sneezed; another coughed. He felt light-headed and just a bit warm, warmer than normal. His muscles and joints ached, which was nothing unusual for a cowboy who had spent the day in his saddle and then slept on the ground. Except he'd been inside all night, not even venturing out to visit the little shack out back. He felt a numbing chill run through his bones, and a little scratch of soreness at the back of his throat.

"I hope I ain't comin' down with somethin'," he muttered to himself. "That's all I need, gettin' sick just before brandin' and the drive. Pug's gonna bust my hump if I can't ride."

"You okay?"

Toy looked through the dim light toward the voice and spied John "Slick" Hammer watching him from across the bunkhouse. Hammer, a seasoned cowhand with more drives under his belt than he cared to admit, sat on the floor, leaned back against his bunk, pulling on his boots. His face was wrinkled and pruned from the sun. His knuckles bulged from having been broken and cracked without the aid of proper medical attention. There was only so much mending the cook could do on the ranch. He was there to fix biscuits and keep the men fed, not to play nursemaid to every little scrape and bruise. Toy could tell arthritis pained Slick. He'd always say Arthur was coming to visit when his hands hurt while trying to curl his rope or tie down a steer.

"Looked like you was fixin' to do a header to the floor," Slick said.

"Just a mite light-headed is all," Toy answered. "Pushed up too quick, I reckon."

But Toy felt a little more than just light-headed. The room began to spin. He held on to the center post to keep from sitting down hard on the floor. He tried to focus his gaze on Hammer, but his vision blurred, transforming the cowboy to a misty ghost.

"What the hell?" he whispered.

"And you're lookin' a touch green around the gills. You might wanna have Cookie spoon ya up a dose of that Castor Oil he keeps hid in the chuck wagon."

"You a doctor now, Slick?"

Toy regretted his snide remark the moment he said it. Old Slick was only trying to help.

"Not me, partner. I just don't want you spreadin' nothin' to me. I got enough troubles of my own without comin' down sick with no creepy cruds."

Toy stumbled back to his bunk, sitting down harder than he'd intended.

"What the hell?" he stammered again as he misjudged the width of his cot and hit his head on the bunkhouse wall. Another chill ran through his body, this time with an intensity that shivered him from head to foot. He felt tired and his muscles ached even more than before. His stomach churned and he feared for a moment he was going to upchuck last night's stew.

"Damn," he said. "I'm beginnin' to feel like somebody whooped me durin' the night and didn't wake me up to tell me about it."

With fisted intensity, Toy rubbed his eyes and leaned back on his old feather pillow, stretching his blanket up over his body. He felt like he'd fallen off his horse and been dragged a while. There was no denying it, he'd come down with something during the night.

"Whatever this is," he muttered, "it's fixin' to beat my ass like a red-headed stepchild."

The sound and smell of someone puking filled the room. Toy stuck his head out from under his blanket just in time to see Jesse Thompson, two bunks down, hurl his supper onto the floor, causing a nausea reflex to spread throughout the bunkhouse. Someone, he couldn't see who, began a hacking cough that sounded as if his lungs would burst. He could hear a few of the other cowboys mutter things such as 'Dear Sweet Jesus', or 'Good God in Heaven', or 'What the hell?' as they lurched for the window. The close quarters of the bunkhouse became saturated with the putrid smell of vomit as, one-by-one, cowboys lost their supper.

About that time, Pug Juneau pushed through the bunkhouse door, ready to roust his branding crew out of their bunks, only to be stopped by the sights, sounds, and odors of sickness. At a glance, Pug took in the scene of men doubled over, retching onto the floor or into whatever container they could find. He spied Toy Pickett peeking out from under his blanket. Joshua Gamble, another of his branding crew, pushed past Pug and stumbled outside into the early morning air. His right hand clutched his belly while last night's stew leaked out around his left hand clamped over his mouth.

Pug immediately recognized what was going on. He'd seen it before and dreaded ever seeing it again. It, or something like it, had driven his family out of New Orleans many years ago when it ravaged the city and lay waste to thousands of lives. It had arrived on sailing ships from ports all over the world, so no one actually knew where it started.

Out here in the Oklahoma Territory, some called it Tick Fever or Typhus, which he knew instinctively this was not the case. And although either could be deadly if not caught and treated immediately, it usually only lasted a week or ten days, then the fever would break as soon as the infection worked its way out of the human body. Others called it Prairie Pox or Prairie Flu. But it didn't matter what they called it, Pug knew this wasn't a simple fever, and it was going to be trouble for the ranch. If the scene in the bunkhouse was any indication, they had a serious problem on their hands. He knew he was witnessing the beginning of a catastrophe, an enemy that knew no boundaries and had no respect for race, color, creed, or cowboy.

"Hammer?" Pug said.

"Yeah, boss."

"You sick?"

"Don't think so, boss," Hammer answered. "Not so's you could tell."

"Get your horse saddled and go fetch the doc from town."

"It's over twenty miles to town, Pug. That'll take damn near all day."

Pug propped the door open then crossed the bunkhouse floor and locked back the window shutters, allowing in the fresh morning air. He turned back to Hammer, a serious expression on his face that Hammer recognized as his don't-give-me-no-lip look.

While Hammer gathered his riding gear, Pug examined each man. He sent those not showing signs of illness outside with their bedrolls and gear into the morning air. Others, he ordered to stay in bed; Toy Pickett among them. He dispatched Harley Drew to the big house to fetch Mr. Marshall. The rancher would need to be informed they were in for a major setback in the branding, and probably the drive.

"Get the doc back here as quick as you can," Pug ordered. "Tell him about these boys havin' fever and losin' their supper. Just tell him New Orleans. He'll know what to do."

"New Orleans? What the hell does that mean?"

"Just do it," Pug ordered. "And hurry."

It took Slick Hammer all day and well into the night before he returned to the ranch with Doc Martin. It wasn't the distance that slowed him, although a straight-through twenty mile ride would take its toll on any cowboy. When he arrived in town a little after noon, he learned the doctor was on a house call delivering a seventh child to Buster Moran and his missus.

It didn't take long to explain the ranch situation to the doctor. When Slick said New Orleans, the doctor set about gathering up a slew of equipment, medicines, pills, and potions. Slick had no idea of their purpose but helped load them onto Doc's two-seater buckboard.

"You ride on ahead and I'll catch up with you at the ranch," Doc said.

Hammer shook his head.

"Nah, I ain't in that much of a hurry. I think I'll ride back to the ranch on the seat of this here buggy. Besides, my backside is plum sore from a full day in the saddle."

Doc Martin knowingly looked Slick up and down.

"Besides," Slick said, "I had me a few shots of rye in the saloon while I was waitin' for you to finish with Mrs. Moran. Might try to catch me a few winks a'sleep on the way home."

When Doc Martin and Slick arrived at the Double-Deuce, Mr. Marshall and Pug had already set up a makeshift camp near the well for the unaffected cowboys. They'd quarantined the rest inside the bunkhouse. The doctor took the scene in at a glance and set about examining each man. They all appeared to have contracted the same malady at about the same time.

"It looks like the flu," he told Pug and Marshall after his initial examinations, "but then again, it don't."

He exchanged a knowing glance with Pug.

"What the hell does that mean?" Marshall asked.

"It means whatever these boys is suffering from started about the same time," he answered. "If so, it could have a standardized incubation period."

The rancher had no idea what the doctor was talking about.

"Could it be food poisoning?" Marshall asked. He hoped it was something as simple as that. Could Cookie have gotten hold of a rank piece of beef and just didn't notice? "They started upchucking last night's stew about daybreak. Now it's just dry heaves."

Doc Martin leaned over Toy Pickett and pushed his left eye open, holding his lantern high enough to reveal the cowboy's bloodshot orb and swollen sinuses. He lay the back of his hand across Toy's forehead and felt a clammy fever working its way through his body. Doc shook his head.

"It's some kind'a infectious malady," he said. "I've never seen this one before, but I've read about it."

"If it ain't food poisoning then it's just the damn flu," Marshall stated matter-of-factly. "These boys is comin' down with a spring flu and will be up and around in a couple'a days. All they need is a hard day in the saddle and this'll blow over."

Doc Martin shook his head again.

"Not this time."

He turned toward Pug Juneau. "You're from New Orleans, aren't you, Pug?"

Pug nodded. He knew where Doc was going with this. He remembered the illness that devastated the coastal city when he was just a boy. If this was the same thing, or anything like it, they were in for trouble. But how could a disease brought in on ships from around the world years ago affect a ranch stuck out in the middle of the Oklahoma panhandle?

"Has anyone from the ranch been away for a while and could'a brought a pox back with them?" Doc asked. "I'd say within the last few weeks."

Both Pug and Marshall answered no.

"But we did have a migrant family stop by the ranch on their way west about three weeks ago," Marshall said.

"Uh-huh."

"They was from some foreign country somewhere. Couldn't hardly understand nothin' they said. Two of their three kids had come down sick, so they stopped by the ranch house begging for medical supplies and a place to rest for a few days. Since we didn't have any medicines, I let'em set up camp behind the bunkhouse so they'd have access to the well for drinking and washing water, and to the outhouse."

This can't be a mere coincidence, Doc thought. And this outbreak can only mean one thing – the migrant family had transported the cause of it onto the ranch. They'd moved on after spending several days, taking their sick kids with them, kids that are probably dead by now.

But what had they left behind? What had they contaminated? Is the well water safe to drink? Will members of the Marshall family and other ranch employees who came in contact with them begin showing signs of illness? How many other people along their path have been exposed to a potentially deadly pandemic? Is the ranch going to die like so much of New Orleans and the Louisiana coastline those many years ago?

Doc Martin laid his hand on Marshall's elbow and led him away from Pug and the sick cowboys. He didn't want to start a panic but knew he had to establish firm control over this situation before it got out of hand.

"Do you know which way that migrant family went?" Doc asked.

"Best I could tell, they went west," Marshall answered. "Said they was headin' for California."

"You're going to have to send a couple of riders after them."

"Riders?"

"And if they're as sick as you say, they won't have gotten far."

"You reckon they're…"

Doc nodded. "Have your men take along a good supply of coal oil."

"Coal oil?"

"And when they find them, they need to burn their bodies, their wagon, and all their belongings. And kill all their livestock and burn them too."

"So you reckon they're dead already?"

"If not, they will be before long. And God help us if they reach a town with any sizable population."

"Ain't much'a nothin' due west'a here accept maybe an Injun camp or two. Apache and Navajo mostly."

After considering Doc Martin's instructions, it dawned on Marshall that the doctor was holding something back from him. He looked around the bunkhouse at the sick men, and out into the yard where the rest of his cowboys had set up camp. He cast a sidelong glance back toward his ranch house and to his wife and oldest of three daughters who had stepped out onto the back porch.

"Doc?" he said. "Are you fearful that whatever them folks brought in here that's got my crew sick could spread to the rest of the ranch, including my family?"

"Anyone who came into direct contact with those people are in grave danger," Doc Martin stated matter-of-factly. Marshall looked back toward the ranch house just in time to see his wife sneeze and wipe her face with a handkerchief she pulled from her apron pocket.

Dawn the next morning saw Slick Hammer and another ranch hand the doctor didn't recognize heading west in pursuit of the migrant family – a family seeking a new life in California, only to find certain death on the Oklahoma prairie. The cowboys led a pack mule laden with containers of coal oil to wipe every trace of the family from existence, and with tools to bury any cinders that might remain. Although he'd warned them to wear bandanas over their mouths and noses, and to thoroughly wash their hands with the bars of lye soap he'd stored in their saddlebags, Doc Martin knew full well the men were in danger of contracting the illness. He only hoped the disease died with the body.

A heavy veil of illness and death fell over the Double-Deuce. The doctor converted the bunkhouse into a quarantine ward, separating the men with walls of blankets. He kept a pot of water boiling on the wood-burning stove and tried to keep every surface and his medical instruments hygienic as possible. He feared the well water may have been contaminated, so he poured a generous quantity of quinine into a bucket and lowered it into the well, hoping the drug would have some stabilizing effect on the ranch's main water supply.

Doc Martin set up a makeshift examination room in a corner with the best light, complete with a lens microscope he'd purchased in Kansas City last year. He still wasn't fully schooled on the workings of how microscopic life could have such devastating effects on the human body. He marveled at the magnificence of God's creations and how the greater does not always conquer the lesser.

Try as he might, the epidemic spread from man to man, and there was nothing he could do about it. Even Cookie lay sequestered in a corner bunk. Doc figured the cook only had a few days to live. He'd prepared his last meal and dealt out his last dose of Castor Oil.

The first cowboy to die from the unknown disease was Joshua Gamble, the cowboy that pushed past Pug the first morning of the epidemic. But he wouldn't be the last. The next was Jesse Thompson, followed by Harley Drew, the cowboy sent to the big house to fetch the boss. Mrs. Marshall and their oldest daughter fell sick almost immediately. It was determined they'd been infected by the migrant family. Both died within hours of each other after laying sick for a week. Why Marshall and his youngest children weren't infected was still a mystery to the doctor.

In total, eighteen ranch hands and family members succumbed to the plague. Against the doctor's orders, the initial unaffected drovers branded and moved their herd to market as planned. Rancher Marshall said they couldn't let the ranch go under based on a few sick people. Doc Martin remembered watching the herd being driven north to connect with railheads that would carry them all over the country. He prayed the illness didn't transmit from animals, and that none of the other drive cowboys were carriers of the deadly disease.

Doc Martin leaned over Toy Pickett stretched out on his bunk, his blanket pulled up around his chin. Pickett's breath was labored and shallow. Sweat glistened on his forehead, his skin clammy to the touch. Pickett's bloodshot eyes stared back at the doctor, unseeing except for a dim reflection from the coal oil lamp hanging on the center post holding up the sod roof.

I'm dyin', Toy thought. I'm dyin' and I don't know why. It ain't like I got drunk in the saloon on payday and got myself shot. And it ain't like I got bucked off a horse and broke my neck, or got trampled in a stampede. I'm just dyin', bein' killed by something that can't be seen. It ain't fair. It ain't right. It ain't...

Doc Martin watched the light fade from Toy Pickett's eyes. How many more would die?

JIM LAUGHTER

Jim Laughter is the creator of the Galactic Axia young adult sci/fi series, the Keller and Morris thriller series, and the Runt – A Cowboy's Story western short story series. His other works include dystopian fiction novel Polar City Red and true crime novel From Victim to Hero – The Untold Story of Steven Stayner. Jim lives in Tulsa, Oklahoma with his wife, Wilma. He is a retired U.S. Air Force Master Sergeant, and a former president of the Tulsa NightWriters. Jim's books and stories are available in eBook format on Amazon.

Lost in a Pandemic Blog

by **Margaret Lee**

Celebrate? Remember?
What word did he use ...
the verb for what we should do
with our strength,
now that we can't do anything;
now that strength
doesn't seem to matter.

He made a collage.
His scraps, leftover pieces,
affirmed what made him strong.
And it helped, he said.
Remind ourselves?
Was that it?
Remind ourselves
that we do have strength?
That we can?

Right now I cannot—
see my children,
go to the drugstore,
        the library,
        the farmer's market;
run screaming out of Oklahoma;
cuddle my grandchildren,
dissolve in an ocean
        of food and friendship
        with those I love ...
so many things.
But I can

feel what happens on other planets.
When tears fall without gravity
in a distant universe,
they land like lead
in my heart.

I can time travel—
walk around a thousand years ago
and see exactly how
we ended up like this.

I can map the route
that determination takes
when it ventures out
from some hidden, interior cave,
    trudges forests of indecision,
    paddles bayous of doubt,
until it opens a person's mouth
and makes them speak.

I can speak foreign languages:
the language of wonder,
of terror,
of seeking;
the language of yearning
    for comfort,
    for quiet,
    for meaning.

I'm even learning
a new language now—
a language of hope.
When I say,
"well, I don't know ..."
it means,
"I think I'll write a poem."
And the poem lives forever.
I guess that's strength enough
right now.

Snagged

by **Margaret Lee**

Brilliant nodes on a web
crackling with electric charges
of talk, touch, propinquity—
that was then.
Now we thrash
like fish in a knotted net
that confines us
without connecting us.

Always invisible,
our genuine bonds have gone slack;
the virus melted them down,
poured them into new molds
in the shapes of computers,
cell phones, doorstep deliveries.
Our three-dimensional concerns,
jumbled emotional toyboxes,
brightly colored thoughts
get pinched, squeezed,
macerated, compressed,
converted to ones and zeroes
to fit through the internet.

If I awaken early
and creep out at dawn,
will shimmering dewdrops
catch the sunlight and reveal,
like twinkle lights,
our hidden web of connection?

If I grow my fingernails long,
can I catch a strand of that web
as I claw the air, the earth,
to find, to feel
the bonds that hold us
together?

Would that this floating fishnet
could become a rocking cradle;
that we could complete the circuit,
feel the charge,
light each other's lives
again.

MARGARET LEE

I am a new poet and aspiring naturalist. I love exploring the Oklahoma prairies, New Mexico deserts, and Oregon coastal forests and seashores. I am retired as Assistant Professor of Humanities at Tulsa Community College in Tulsa. I have earned a Bachelor of Arts in History from Seattle University, a Master of Divinity from Phillips Theological Seminary in Tulsa, and a Doctor of Theology from the Melbourne College of Divinity in Melbourne, Australia. I have written about the Greek language and New Testament in books and academic journals. I belong to the Tulsa NightWriters, the Oklahoma Writers Federation, Inc., and the American Academy of Poets.

Disconnection

by Sid Martin

Or, What I've Learned From The Corona Crisis.

Well, the first thing I learned is that the official name for my lifestyle is "quarantine." That's right. Stay home, don't go out. I've been quarantining for years and never knew it. Maybe that's why I'm so healthy. Or not. They used to call it being anti-social. Now it's called social distancing. I'm not an introvert. I'm socially distant. No hugs, no bugs. Six feet back, not six feet under. I figure, better cabin fever than the fever cabin, ICU. Tulsa's new park, the Gathering Place, is now the Distancing Place. March Madness? Try March Sadness. And the NBA became the National Bannedball Association. Church is closed but I learned that the Tenth Commandment really reads, "Thou shalt not COVID thy neighbor." And students? If you go through virtual graduation, does that mean you virtually, not actually, graduated? Time will tell.

Another lesson I learned was that there's such a thing as being too stocked up. Let's face it. Toilet paper hoarders are shitty people. Just saying. I also learned that a martini in quarantine is a quarantini. I'd add a Corona chaser. My motto: Don't whine, drink wine.

And essential work? Who's to say? I'm a lawyer. I still go to work. A law office is essential. If you bitch about it, we'll sue. My son is a heat and air technician. He's essential because, hey, who's going to stay home without air conditioning? And who says barbers aren't essential? We're all going to look like Bigfoot before long.

The problem with masks is that you can't see what a person looks like. That's why robbers wear them. It must be easy to hold up a store now. No one would notice you're wearing a mask. What kills me is people wearing bandanas as masks, like bandits. "Hands up! Social distancing or your life!" Personally, I don't wear one, a mask that is, not a bandana. Maybe I should. It would hide my face. Could be an improvement. People are getting creative. You can use a coffee filter as a coughie filter. One lady designed a mask with a clear plastic window over the mouth so deaf people can read their lips. A woman on television said she was only going to put makeup on the upper part of her face and wear a mask. Say, if you're not supposed to touch your face, you can't put on makeup anywhere then. Perhaps someone should come up with a mask that reproduces a photo of a person's lower face. Then you could see who you're talking to.

I've decided to take a musical approach to social distancing. We have to go our "Separate Ways." If you see someone on the street, just "Walk On By." If a person comes up to you, "Walk Away, Renee." If a stranger tries to "Stand By Me," I say "Don't Stand So Close to Me." If they get close enough to "Lean on Me," I tell them "Beat It." If a cute girl says, "I Want to Hold Your Hand," I say "U Can't Touch This." After all, we "Don't Get Around Much Anymore." This quarantine business could last "A Long, Long Time," but that's "How to Save a Life." It's about "Stayin' Alive." Just remember, "Someday We'll Be Together." If you want to "Party in the USA," you've "Got to Give it Up." I've got to stay in "The House that Built Me." I live on "Lonely Street." That's why "I'm So Lonesome I Could Cry." "Only the Lonely -- Know the Way I Feel Tonight." I just say "Hello, Walls." Maybe you have to stay with the "Old Folks at Home." If you're stuck with a quaranteen, you may go "Crazy." But if you're lucky and have a significant other, remember, "Girls Just Want to Have Fun." Your house can be a regular "Love Shack." Along about Christmas, you'll be saying "Sweet Child o' Mine." Which reminds me. We can expect a huge crop of COVID kids. The new Baby Boomers, or is it Baby Zoomers?

SID MARTIN

Sid Martin is an attorney who specializes in legal research and writing. He also has a theology degree and published a commentary on the Gospel of Mark. He is writing a series of murder/suspense/thrillers starring investigative reporter Chet Waters. The debut novel, *Death at Dawn,* is with an agent. He hopes the agent sells it as he is too lazy to self-publish.

An Unknown Deadly Species

by **Rae Carter Neal**

An unknown deadly species came forth
Lurking among the world's population.
It was not satisfied to linger in the open.
A place to hide, to burrow, to multiply,
And change lives were its vicious goals.

Invisible, yet determinedly destructive,
The species searched and waited
For a host to unknowingly offer it a home.
It longed for a human being to touch it
With their hands spread wide-open.

It is so like humans to touch their faces,
Rub their eyes, wipe their noses,
And use their fingers to cram food
Into the cavity of their mouths.
Hands became vehicles of transportation.

Given the opportunity, species rode hands
And slipped into human facial crevices.
Once inside, species quickly slid downward,
Down into the lungs to take up residence,
To wreak havoc upon our human bodies.

In the years 2019 and 2020, a species came.
Why it chose China to manifest is unknown.
People became sick; many survived, some died.
Soon it leaped across country borders
And over continental seas and oceans.

Medical scientists declared it a coronavirus
And eventually, someone named it COVID-19.
Its mission appeared to be to destroy mankind,
But such species underestimate human curiosity,
The insatiable desire to comprehend anomalies.

What can a pandemic virus accomplish?
It can creep into psyches and create fear,
Travel across borders and invade countries
Without military generals at the helm of armies.
It can eliminate sports events to prevent
Basketballs from dropping through hoops and
Footballs from crossing goal lines and
Flying over goal posts to increase scores.

The virus is outrageous with its action
Of death upon the bodies of humans to
Reduce family structures and future
Picnic reunions. Ancestral rolls grow.
It prefers to prey upon the elderly, but
Has no conscience to remove a baby
From its mother's breast or a young
Student from the swing of a playground.

A virus vies for prominence in governing,
Takes over leaders' concerns to top their
Agendas and news conferences. Even during
Phone conversations between enemy
Heads of state, the virus grabs the priority
Of subjects discussed leaving differences of
Political biases to wander from consciousness.
Such is its jealousy for everyone's attention.

Prayers flew upward; scientists viewed test tubes,
Learned the habits, maneuverings, and structure
Of COVID-19, its vulnerabilities, and enemies.
God brought illumination to minds of virologists.
Discoveries dawned in many labs of microbes

Which did battle to uncover and kill the invader.
Imagine the surprise of the ferocious species, the
Enemy of the century, when attacked by vaccines.

By faith, we declare:
Thus, it is squashed, terminated, eradicated,
The natural world and human beings freed
To live life once again in victory without fear.
The plague of the viral enemy is conquered,
COVID-19 eliminated. The war is won.

Psalm 91:9-10, *"⁹Because you have made the Lord, which is my refuge, even the most High, your habitation; ¹⁰There shall no evil befall you, neither shall any plague come near your dwelling."* NKJV

RAE CARTER NEAL

Rae Carter Neal, an ordained minister, pastored churches in southern Spain and on Grand Canary Island, Spain; launched and taught in Victory Bible Institute in St. Petersburg, Russia, only five months after the Iron Curtain fell; worked as a missionary in Slovakia, Costa Rica, in mountain villages of Guatemala, and other countries.

Rae majored in Rhetoric and Writing at Tulsa University and Ministerial Studies at Global University in Springfield, Missouri.

Her first book, Midnight Melodies: From the Seas and Rivers of Life, contains international award-winning poetry and is available on Amazon. Her second book, Daylight Melodies: Poetry to Inspire, Empower, and Encourage, will be released in the fall of 2020.

Cecilia

by **Sue Cory Person**

Her appearance was flawless—short-cropped hair with wispy black bangs framing eyes filled to the brim with lashes. To most, she was perfect.

But Cecilia Sanchez was drowning in sadness.

A stealthy escape was the plan, surely that would shake things up. Maybe wake *him* up. Her husband of five years was rarely home, and when he was—he wasn't. That was a deal-breaker for Cecilia.

Pushing the confirmation number into her wallet, she gulped down the last bit of her favorite wine, Harvey and Harriet. She'd bought plenty to numb the anxiety of leaving Ricardo on Valentine's Day. This time she would do it: she'd be gone when Ricardo returned home from his three-day weekend shift.

Ricardo was the beloved Chief of Staff at San Francisco's Public Hospital. He lived to help people. A striking man in every sense of the word. Well-mannered with a tender heart and a warm smile. He had a way of making others feel special, even before speaking.

She'd never met such a handsome gentleman. Not in high school or college, and certainly not in her wild days of modeling on the streets of Milan. A Medical Super Hero is how she'd described him to her family. And it was the same unselfish heroism that drew Cecilia into his world. But that was long before she realized the hidden snare.

A Super Hero is always busy saving others.

The Plan

Surprising her sister was first on Cecilia's stealthy-escape destination list. Five years older, Patrice was an old soul. Getting married right out of high school was her aspiration, and she'd achieved it. With five children delivered in seven years, she was living a full and happy life. Regrettably, her husband, Michael, wasn't the financial success Ricardo was, so they lived barely above poverty. Nonetheless, he was an excellent father and husband.

Cecilia had fibbed to her niece, twelve-year-old Sapphire, in a recent face-time call. "I need your new address. I'm sending a gift to celebrate your dad's rise to an upper-level position." He'd risen from sanitary worker to Waste Management Consultant. It was a promotion to be proud of, and Cecilia was bringing a gift, but the secrecy of her plan to leave Ricardo needed their new address without questions. Patrice would be the first person Ricardo called.

Italy

From the moment Alitalia's Airbus landed, things were peculiar and unfamiliar. Airport security was checking the temperature of every person exiting and entering. Cecilia had relaxed aboard the plane, even paying extra for the Magnifica Class, but now her insides jittered with anxiety as she waited for a taxi. Something was wrong.

The taxi driver never spoke a word until he groaned and stopped six feet from the curb. "This is no place for a woman to be left alone." He continued in a louder than appropriate rant. "At one time, the Rossetti and Giselle were an expensive place to live. The city took over, and as you can see, they're just a menace to Milan, a place for the homeless to gather."

"Well, my sister lives here," Cecilia said, scrunching her nose to exit. A musty fog floated across the lane from the three-story, vintage-stone buildings—both fully coated with green mildew. Across the water-way, industrial chimneys were puffing large plumes of smoke into the hillside skyline. It was not what she'd pictured for her sister.

Cecilia prayed for the inside of the building to be better than the outside. The prayer deferred when a man came running toward her. Never looking up, he scribbled words on a cardboard square. "Affamati" (Hungry) was all Cecilia could untangle from his slurred attempt at Italian.

"Enter at your own risk," he finally said in English, throwing the sign when he didn't get the desired reaction of a donation. In a swirl of movement, Cecilia saw the red government icon on the back. He'd repurposed an official sign.

Feeling a twinge of guilt, Cecilia dug through her purse. "Do you know if Patrice Shaos lives here?"

"That might be her name; I didn't ask."

One tooth shined when he opened his mouth to click his tongue at her tossed euro note. Cecilia turned for the entrance when he changed his focus to her legs.

"I wouldn't go in there!" he yelled when crumbling scroll-work fell to the sidewalk as a second warning. A plaque was still solidly attached: Rossetti suites, it said. 1401 Blueberry Drive. The address matched what she had written.

"I need to see if that's my sister."

"Don't say I didn't warn you," he said.

Cecilia covered her mouth while she read the eviction notice tacked to the partially ajar door. A putrid odor was drifting from inside.

She pushed it open.

The far-reaching hall was in shambles, strewn clothes, and trash on the floor—nailed boards blocked a stairwell going up, from floor to ceiling.

The smell was one she'd never encountered before.

"Hello," she called through the hall, aiming her words to the open door of the first apartment. "I'm looking for Patrice Shaos?"

A scampering began inside. Cecilia kept her eyes on the larger than a standard doorway, stretching to look inside.

"Hello? Is anyone here?"

The distant wall had a bed occupied.

"Hello, I'm looking for my sister."

Rats of every size spilled to the floor, scattering like ants at her scream.

Cecilia pulled the door shut. "Surely, the address is wrong. Patrice wouldn't live like this."

In a moment of quiet recovery, Cecilia heard crying from down the hall.

That was encouraging.

The crying voice had no resemblance to her sister, but maybe she knows Patrice and her family.

Cecilia stepped inside after her knock on the partly open door produced a raspy cry of defiance.

"Just leave an old woman alone to die in peace!"

The room smelled of urine and feces. Centered in the living room was a full-sized bed, and the body beneath a moth-eaten blanket shimmied with movement.

"I'm not going to hurt you," Cecilia said.

A fuzzy head popped through a hole in the blanket. "Who are you?"

"I'm Cecilia Sanchez. I'm looking for my sister, Patrice?"

"Everybody's gone. Didn't you see the sign?"

"The eviction notice?"

"No. The red one. The building and everyone inside are detained, even the dead. The city just left me here with the dead people. I heard the man say so."

Cecilia's concern for her sister moved beyond living conditions. "Did anyone go to the hospital?"

Creeping closer, she looked the woman over. Without a doubt, she didn't look well, but she was a little too spunky to be dying. "You need to go to the hospital if you think you're dying. I'll call an ambulance."

Before Cecilia could find her phone, a repetitive hammering trembled the walls.

"Too late. The man told me they'd be locking us inside tonight, till the virus is gone."

Cecilia ran through the hallway to see the entrance blocked with yellow and red bands. "Wait! I'll be leaving! I just came to find my sister!"

"Sorry, missy, direct orders from the top. No one can leave this building. The street is barricaded. Both units, Rossetti and Giselle, are quarantined until the pandemic is over."

This can't be happening. Cecilia stared into his face until she understood it was happening, and there was nothing she could do about it. "Well, how long will that be?"

"When the Prime Minister gives the order, I suppose." He peered through a gap in the tape and softened his voice. "The food pantry will come by once a week and leave supplies on the step. Stay away from the door, or they'll remove you from the route."

Cecilia backed up. No food would be a death sentence for sure.

Cecilia's expensive phone was blinking in more than one place when she turned it on. Eight missed calls, twenty-three messages, and a red-light displaying short battery life. She'd turned her phone off before she arrived at the San Francisco International Airport. Her decision to leave her husband was pure rebellion, and she didn't want to answer for her actions, at least not until she reached Italy.

She dialed her husband, Ricardo, surprised at his quick answer. "I've been trying to reach you, Ceil, where are you?"

"I'm in Milan, at the Rossetti. I wanted to see my family. My phone is almost dead, and I forgot my charger. Ricardo, they quarantined me."

"Are you sick?"

"No. But I'm with a lady who says she is and some of her neighbors died from it. The Rossetti is under lockdown."

His silence scared Cecilia. "Ricardo?"

"I wish you would have talked to me before you left. If you're having a problem, I'll do anything to fix it."

Hearing the quiver in his voice pierced her insides. "I know, I'm sorry."

"Ride this thing out, Cecilia. Cover your face and stay away from anyone with a fever. This virus is bad. Nothing we've tried can stop it. The CDC says the world will be coming to a standstill till we do."

The last words Cecilia heard. "I love you, babe. . . ."

"I love you too," she whispered to a dead phone.

"My name is Margo, what's yours?"

Cecilia lifted her gaze to the wide-eyed, fuzzy-headed woman and began thinking of a way to be polite but ask a critical question. "I'm Cecilia. My apologies for being so audacious; do you have a fever?"

"I think so. And I feel terrible like somebody whipped me with a stick." She lifted her wool blanket to show bright pink marks on her stomach.

"How long have you had the whelps?"

"Whelps? I didn't know I had whelps, must be from my scratching. I've been soaking in the tub to ease the itching."

"What have you been eating?"

She was so thin every bone in her body was well-defined. Cecilia assumed the answer would be nothing, but Margo opened a pillowcase to show a stash of food. A mega-sized box of saltine crackers and a large can of government-issued peanut butter. When she unsnapped the lid and pulled a spoon into view, she offered Cecilia a bite.

"No. But thank you. I think I'll see if any of your neighbors will answer the door now."

Cecilia walked the halls. The second set of stairs was removed at head-height, making them useless, and no answer to her banging on apartments two through nine. Rats scurried around her feet. There was no place to sit, and when the time came, no place to sleep.

∞∞∞∞∞

Maybe Margo had the virus, and maybe not. She'd been smiling from ear to ear since she figured out she would have company till this thing was over. It seemed Cecilia's only option was to stay with Margo, and it wasn't a comforting decision. The stark reality was, except for a nightstand, Margo's bed was the only elevation from the cracked linoleum, where roaches proclaimed ownership.

Cecilia stood as long as she could, then sat on the bed at Margo's insistence. She pondered about Margo's over-the-top delight at someone being there.

"Do you have family?" Cecilia asked.

"No. My Benny died before we had children. He went to war and never returned."

"Any sisters or brothers?"

Margo's head shook. "I had a cousin that lived here with me. That's her in the fancy box."

A curled finger pointed to a picture beside an alabaster container next to the bed. The gold inscription said, 'Ruby.'

"Did she die from the virus?"

"No. She's been gone since the eighties."

"I'm sorry about your husband and cousin. I'm sure it's been lonely without them."

"A little." Margo readjusted to see the picture. "Ruby and I fought like sisters, and she was mean like the devil, but we got each other through a lot of years."

Tensions eased, and conversation flowed. Margo and Cecilia talked about everything in a person's life. Love, marriage, politics, religion, Ruby, and Benny. Lots about Benny. Margo was talking long after Cecilia fell asleep.

At first light, Cecilia strained to hold her breath and ignore a family of roaches climbing the wall by the door. A usual waking in her condo delivered a euphoria lasting long past her shower and morning coffee on the veranda.

Oh, how she wished to open her eyes to four sections of glass with a view to the garden displaying a vast array of exotic plants and flowers. A picture so mesmerizing any artist would be proud to replicate.

That life, her life, was a far cry from the dingy, tall-walled room her eyes sluggishly blinked at. She and Margo were sharing the only bed, and so far, not one rat had tried to join them.

Stretching her eyes from the lazy blink, Cecilia saw Margo standing on the nightstand peeking through a tall and narrow, boarded-up window. When the stool started to sway, Cecilia swooped in to catch Margo before she hit the wood floor. Margo jumped from Cecilia's arms to grab a pen and spiral notebook next to Ruby's picture.

"Twenty-seven thousand, seven hundred and forty!" she said, letting the pencil drop.

Cecilia was alarmed at her erratic actions, but even more alarmed at how hot Margo felt in her arms. Then came the blood from her nose.

"Did I bump your nose?" Cecilia asked.

"No. I get nose bleeds. The nurse said it's when my blood pressure is in over-load."

"Do you take medicine?"

"I did. The nurse quit coming last month."

"What's that number you wrote down?"

She picked the spiral up, put the pencil inside, and closed the cover. "After my Benny died, Ruby said to watch every sunrise and write it down, a sure sign I'm still living. It gives me a reason to get up every day."

Listening to Margo made Cecilia feel ashamed at how small her own problems were. And listen she did, a year-by-year accounting, till each day ended and both fell asleep. Margo only stopped talking during her peanut butter break, twice a day.

The stories Margo told were some Cecilia would never forget. It portrayed love in a simpler time, a love most dream of having, including Cecilia.

Margo and Benny's three years of dating and one year of marriage frolicked like a good book inside Cecilia's head, a visual that would live forever. The last thing Benny told Margo before boarding the train for war-stricken Sicily continually stirred tears. "If I don't come back, meet me under God's rainbow, I'll be waiting for you."

∞∞∞∞∞∞

Ricardo was a good man, Cecilia determined that the first day she met him. He was strong and confident, but he'd taken on more than he'd bargained for when he married a wife who needed a lot of attention. With a full schedule at the hospital and charity cases after hours, he was barely coming home. A voice inside said he was avoiding his needy wife, and Cecilia believed it. She had accepted her role of being more of a hassle than an asset to the man she adored.

A self-spoiled princess, created by design, the world revolved around Cecilia, and at eighteen, she decided to live her life as a full-fledged, bona fide Queen. No kids for her. No sharing of time, money, or the man she would someday marry. And so far, she'd stayed true to that philosophy. While Ricardo worked long hours at the hospital, Cecilia kept herself and their four-thousand square foot condo in near perfect condition. The thought of someone like Margo, living in such filth, never crossed her mind.

Margo was snoring. And sleeping so close, their bodies touched. (A situation that took Cecilia two days to finally deal with.) She had scooted a safe distance away, and Margo moved

89

back to reconnect. After several days of bonding, Cecilia felt love for the strange and quirky woman who wasn't sure what year it was but thought she was getting close to her ninety-sixth birthday. Cecilia reached to lift a fuzzy strand of wet hair from Margo's cheek. When releasing a held breath, her eyes filled with tears. She couldn't imagine the horror of living like this for a good part of one's life, as Margo has. A fate worse than death.

When the pandemic was over, life would be different. She'd make things right with Ricardo and everyone else, including Margo. She didn't have a set plan, but money was no problem. Even if she had to move Margo to California, this child-like woman wouldn't be alone, fighting the roaches and rats anymore.

Margo coughed through the night. The severity alarmed Cecilia but also reassured her she was still alive. The wheezing worsened shortly before daybreak and became more of a whistle when Margo's lungs struggled for air. Cecilia touched her forehead, accidentally waking her.

"You're too hot, Margo. We better get you into the tub."

"Not yet, it's time for the sunrise." Margo tried to move without success.

"Let me lift you." Cecilia pushed the nightstand below the window and tried to help Margo over. Wobbling, thin legs collapsed Margo to the bed. Cecilia picked her up and cradled her like a baby.

Margo snuggled against Cecilia's collarbone and admired her beauty. "You look like an angel. I dreamed you were. Are you an angel?"

Cecilia smiled at Margo's sweet child-like evaluation before she spoke. "The sun is rising, you better hurry or you'll miss it."

When Margo turned, a quick jerk of excitement stirred her body. "I see it," she whispered, "it's under the beautiful rainbow. Can you see the rainbow?"

Cecilia saw a clear morning sky with blue and orange clouds surrounding the rising sun. "I don't see a rainbow, but it is quite colorful."

"It's a rainbow. The best one I've ever seen. Do you think my Benny is there?"

Margo's eyes were hazy when she turned at Cecilia's silence.

It was less than a moment, but to Cecilia, it seemed an eternity,

Margo's body seized in pain.

Cecilia held Margo close. "Don't be afraid; I'm here; everything is going to be fine."

When the shudder stopped, Cecilia stepped to the floor, still holding Margo. "And you know what? If Benny is under that rainbow, he'll wait for you. There's no rush."

Margo stretched toward Cecilia's ear and whispered. "Thank you for coming; I was so afraid I'd go alone."

Cecilia spoke the words her heart decided the night before. "I love you, Margo, and I promise you'll never be alone again."

Peaceful and smiling, Margo's eyes closed.

Cecilia held her close enough to feel a faint heartbeat. That gave her hope. But then it stopped.

Meeting the tiny woman had changed everything in Cecilia's life. She now understood Ricardo's obsession with helping others, and his resolve to be a hero.

Before the next sunrise, Cecilia heard voices. Someone was trying to get in. She moved to the hallway to listen to what sounded like an argument. "If you enter, you can't leave till the quarantine is over!"

Ricardo's voice bellowed with half English and half Italian. "I'm going inside! I'm a doctor doing my job!"

∞∞∞∞∞∞

Margo was buried next to Benny. Cecilia ordered a rainbow headstone that stretched to both and made arrangements for flowers to be delivered weekly.

She and Ricardo bought the Rossetti and Giselle from the city and renovated all sixty suites designated for the elderly. Once again, the buildings were an elegant place to live. Twice a year, Ricardo, Cecilia, and their two children pay a visit to oversee the health and well-being of the residents.

When an experience is so intense it pricks your heart and clears your vision, it is a gift from God.

The end

SUE CORY PERSON

Someone once said, "The only prerequisite to becoming a writer is to have something worthwhile to write about. I decided that included me. I have five books published in Middle-Grade. I've been told I write with heart, and that's enough to keep me going.

Sue Cory Person

Love Letter to 2020

by **Cindy Rose**

From behind the mask I draw ragged breath

And write of fears and tears.

Under the gloves my nails hide, ragged from clinging

To what never was and what never can be.

Dreams persist like storms on a hot summer afternoon.

Lingering heavy as humidity, they wait for a breeze

To shift the pressure and lift burdens strapped to my chest.

If I could loosen the ties rooting me to this place, this time,

I would snap a photo of how heirloom peonies smell

And sniff the shades of orange in the sunset.

Rhythm of the Night

by Cindy Rose

It's 3:00 a.m. and the doorbell rings. I groan myself awake, unable to grasp how Jerry, my husband, can sleep through the chimes. I'm annoyed, but not too worried. I know from the sound that it's my father ringing for me from the next room, not some stranger at the front door.

I grab my glasses and toddle to my dad's room, flashlight in hand. I can't ask him what he wants, not from the doorway. He is deaf. It doesn't matter. He can talk. When he wants to.

"Ice water."

My heart falls. I go to his side and talk loudly in his right ear. "You can't have anything to drink, Dad. It's the myasthenia gravis. It took away your swallowing. The water would go into your lungs, and you would get pneumonia. Again."

I fetch a sponge swab and run tap water over it, then give it to him. Not enough water to swallow, but enough to wet his mouth.

I shuffle back to bed, eyes burning with unshed tears. I remember my childhood when he did the parenting. I would ask for things he didn't have or couldn't provide, like a new Barbie.

"And people in hell want ice water." He wasn't mean about it. Just matter of fact. Probably never imagined himself at 92 living in a sort of hell on earth.

It's been six years since the aspiration pneumonia that should have killed him, would have killed a lesser man. Six years since everything he ingests goes through a feeding tube. Six years of trading off nights with Jerry to tend to his needs.

I settle into a light sleep listening to Jerry's steading breathing, envious that he can compartmentalize his cares at night and sleep deeply.

The doorbell rings again. My eyes spring open and search out the clock. 4:45 a.m. My mind is wide awake but my body sluggish. The doorbell rings again before I can weave down the hall, one hand on the wall to steady my way.

I turn on the bedside lamp and look at Daddy. He's looking back at me. "You should wear a mask," he says, his voice cracked with dryness.

"Why?" I ask into the better of his ears.

"The bad virus. I might have it. Don't want you to get it."

Sometimes he amazes me with what he retains from watching the news. His dementia is somewhere on the scale beyond senior moments but not yet to Alzheimer's. He doesn't remember that his TV died two days ago and that we got him a new one, or the name of the woman who has been his caregiver for six years. But tonight, he remembers COVID-19.

"You don't have the virus, Dad." I'm worried that my voice might wake Jerry, but I have to take the chance. Daddy's talkative times are few and far between, and I cling to them when they come.

"Is your mother in heaven?" he asks.

I nod and hand him the laminated program from her funeral service that we keep on his bedside table. It shows she died two Christmases ago, and they had been married 70 years.

"It won't be long and I'll be there, too." His voice is but a whisper.

"Mom will be glad to see you, but I'll miss you." What else can I say? I don't want him clinging to this life if he doesn't want to, bedridden, hooked to a food pump, reliant on others to tend to his every need. But I don't want to hurry him along, either. I'm grateful I'm not the One who tracks the number of his days.

"Turn on my blanket. I'm cold."

I smile. Something I can control. I go to the foot of his bed and turn the blanket to number two. The controller has to be beyond his reach or he would cook himself with the heat set on four or five. The last thing he needs is to get sweaty under his covers. His skin, sensitive to the lightest touch, tends to break down easily enough as it is.

"Linda will be here in a couple of hours to take care of you, Dad," I say into his ear. "Go back to sleep."

"Who's Linda?"

Before I can answer, he's talking again. "You look tired. Go back to bed."

"Okay. I love my daddy."

"I love my daughter."

I collapse into bed, pull the covers to my chin, and glance at the clock. 5:15. I know I won't get back to sleep. I close my eyes anyway. Easier to see the memories that way. The Chatty Cathy doll he bought for me on the black market. Using corn kernels at the lake to catch perch after perch. Building a Christmas tree out of tumbleweeds, and flocking it with fake snow.

Memories of my daddy I hold tight. And let go those of the stranger in the night.

CINDY ROSE

Cindy Rose has been writing since her teenage years, and has a B.A. from the University of Tulsa in Rhetoric and Writing. While at TU, she published poetry in *Nimrod* magazine, and later published several confession stories in *True Story* and *Modern Romance* magazines. Over the years she has entered many contests, garnering a number of prizes, including First Place in the Tulsa NightWriters' 1990 Warm-up Contest, First Place in the NightWriters 1991 Annual Best Sellers Contest (Romance Novel category), Third Place in the Mystery/Suspense category of the Oklahoma Writers Federation Inc. contest in 1997, and finalist in the Contemporary Fiction Category of the 2010 Genesis contest sponsored by the American Christian Fiction Writers. In 2018, Cindy was downsized into early retirement from her paralegal job with an oil and gas company, and is now dedicating her time to working on a novel in the women's fiction genre and writing personal essays and poetry. She serves as Editor of *NightScripts*, the newsletter of The Tulsa NightWriters Club. When not writing, she tends to 103 houseplants, Molly, a spoiled and rowdy black lab, and incredibly supportive husband, Jerry. When the writing muse grows quiet, she turns her artistic energies toward making quilts and other fabric creations.

Stranger in the Mask

by **Charles Sasser**

Chronically troubled and restless in the long aftermath of the ongoing quarrel between herself and her husband, Joni had dozed off in the TV room watching a late film on the *Classic Movies* channel when the front door unlocking woke her.

"David?"

He cast a glance at Joni as he adjusted the surgical PPE mask that covered the lower half of his face and continued on down the shadowed hallway to the guest bedroom he had occupied since their blowout nearly three weeks ago. She sprang to her feet and rushed into the hallway after him.

She hesitated. Why was he wearing his mask in the house?

Something about him seemed *different*. He walked with a slower, more awkward gait as though he might have been drinking. His hair appeared darker than usual, and she could have sworn he had worn a red shirt instead of a black one when he abruptly walked out hours ago following another brief flare-up between them.

She blinked her eyes to help adjust them to the dim hallway lighting.

David entered the guest room without looking back and closed the door abruptly behind him. The inside lock clicked into place. Joni batted back tears.

The dreaded COVID-19 pandemic, the deadliest plague in U.S. history with its masks, social distancing, job layoffs, quarantines, and forced home lock downs showed no signs of ending. Families and children forced together into isolation month after month with no relief in sight had led to unbearable tensions that produced quarreling, spousal and child abuse, suicides, and other equally dangerous signs of family and social breakdown. Mobs downtown howled out of control while looting, committing arson, and assaulting police. Crime rates soared in formerly safe neighborhoods.

Before the China Virus turned the world dark and threatening, Joni and David had never seriously quarreled during the four years of their courtship and marriage. Then, due to the pandemic, David got laid off at the factory and they disagreed over whether they should pack up and move to a safer location out West. Joni dug in and refused to consider leaving her aging parents behind alone and isolated to cope with the virus.

"You're pregnant, Joni," David argued. "We have to think of the baby."

"I'm barely a month in," Joni shot back. "Who knows when this will end?"

Even though David had now returned safely home to the guest bedroom, still without any explanation as to where he had been, Joni remained too upset to go to bed. She returned to the TV room to watch a midnight *Classic Movie* starring Gary Cooper. She was dozing off when the buzz of her cellphone almost shook her out of her recliner.

"Yes. *Yes?*"

"Joni, it's Marsha. I noticed your light on. There's a strange car parked down the street. Are you okay?"

"I'm fine, Marsha. Thanks." Marsha served as the neighborhood busybody. Nothing escaped her scrutiny. "I've been watching TV and David's home now. Is there something you needed?"

"Turn on the local news, Joni. There's a killer loose in town. He just a little while ago shot and robbed somebody down by the old Quik Trip store on Memorial. Keep your doors locked, Joni."

"We'll be all right, Marsha."

She hung up and checked the front door to make sure David had bolted it when he came home. Through the security window she glimpsed a patrol car easing past. It stopped next to a dark sedan parked at the curb between houses. A policeman got out and shined his flashlight into the car. By the time Joni thought of going out to tell the officer that the car was strange to the neighborhood, he had remounted and cruised on down through the neighborhood.

She sighed, turned off the TV and thought to check on David again before she went to bed. She knocked on his door and heard him mumble irritably.

"I'm going to bed," she announced through the closed door.

She undressed in the bedroom she now occupied alone, inhaled a deep sigh and slipped underneath covers, exhausted from having waited up so long for her husband to come home. She fell asleep immediately.

Only to be abruptly startled awake when her bedroom door crashed in. Crying out in fear, she sprang upright to find David's shadow looming in the doorway.

"What are you *doing?*" she demanded.

He switched on the overhead light with his free hand; in his other fist he pointed a gun directly at her.

"*David!*"

The protest froze in her throat. He was no longer wearing his PPE mask—and, shockingly, this man was *not* David. The sharp stench of alcohol blasted her from across the room.

She pushed herself as far as she could across the bed and against the wall. Her heart beat furiously in terror. She opened her mouth to scream a warning to David, who must be still asleep. The stranger emitted a mirthless chuckle and warned her with a wave of the gun to keep quiet.

It struck her that this must be the man she took for David returning home. It would have been easy enough to have done so in the unlighted hallway and his wearing a mask. He was about David's size and build with hair of the same general color and style.

"Thought you had seen the last of me, huh?" the stranger taunted. "I got news for you, bitch. That moron you call a husband is dead. I promised I'd do it and I did. You got the same thing coming when we've finished our business."

Joni's heart seemed to collapse in the sudden realization that David might be the victim featured on the local news that Margie was talking about. That meant this stranger in her bedroom was the subject of the police manhunt in the neighborhood. The intruder tossed a wallet on the bed next to her in such a way that it fell open. Joni wept harder when she recognized David's driver's license in its little window.

"I took your husband's ID. It'll take cops the rest of the night to identify the corpse," the stranger gloated. "By then you and me will have finished and you can join him." Joni clasped David's wallet to her breast.

"Look at me, bitch!" the stranger snapped. "I want you to remember me before you die. *Look at me!"*

She suddenly recognized him: one of David's co-workers at the factory. He had been to their house before the COVID-19 lock downs when she and David hosted a workers get-together. She recalled his name now—*Nathan!*

Nathan had got drunk that night and maneuvered Joni off to himself in a corner and began greedily groping her. David walked in on them and tossed him out of the house. Nathan slobbered revenge as he staggered off into the darkness.

"And the bitch!" he vowed. "I'll get her too!"

Nathan was subsequently fired from the plant for misbehavior on the job. Revenge must have been festering in him all this time. Tonight he apparently managed to corner David on one of the virus-deserted streets near the old Quik Trip where he wrangled details of David and Joni's domestic troubles before murdering David and taking his wallet and keys.

He had bided his time in the guest room, which he knew about from the earlier get-together, before he crept out to Joni's bedroom and revealed himself. Joni's heart pounded and tears streamed down her cheeks as he advanced toward her from the door he had kicked in, gun in one hand while he unbuckled his trousers with the other hand and kicked them aside.

"No! Please!" Joni wailed.

He snagged her by the arm and jerked her across the bed toward him. At the same time he tossed his gun aside on the floor, ripped off her night gown, and pounced on top of her naked body snickering like a mad dog. Joni felt herself blacking out from grief and fear.

Suddenly, two policemen charged into the room, weapons ready.

"Let her go!"

Nathan threw himself off the bed onto the floor and scrambled to retrieve his discarded revolver. Shots exploded from the officers' automatic weapons. Bullets ripped into Nathan, convulsing his body.

"David. . . *David!"* Joni screamed and hung her head in prayer.

"Lord, please forgive me. And please let my husband know I love him and I'm sorry. . ."

One of the policeman, an older man, stepped over Nathan's body and pulled a blanket over Joni. "David sent you the same message," he said.

It took her a moment to comprehend. The breath froze in her lungs.

"David?"

"He's on his way to the hospital. He's going to be okay. Thanks to him we learned what this perp was all about and got here in time."

* * * *

CHARLES SASSER

●●●

Charles W. Sasser is a full-time freelance writer, journalist and photographer since 1979. A veteran of both the U.S. Navy (journalist) and U.S. Army (Special Forces, the Green Berets), he was also a police officer in Miami, Florida, for four years, and a police homicide detective with the Tulsa Police Dept. for ten years. He is author of more than 60 published book and at least 3,000 magazine articles and short stories in publication ranging from GUIDEPOSTS to SOLDIER OF FORTUNE.

Right Time, Right Place

by **Kathlyn Carter Smith**

Mike Hudson came into the kitchen from plowing the fields for planting. He walked past his wife, Carol, without speaking and opened the fridge for a cold lemonade. He turned to find her going through the day's mail.

Hot, tired, and hungry, he wasn't in the mood to continue the argument they'd been having for weeks. "Just pay the minimum. We'll catch up later with the rest."

She didn't look up. "I can't stand this. Look at this pile of bills. School loans, the cars, credit cards. Where are we going to get the money to pay these? We've never been in debt until this year." Carol lifted the pile and then dropped it on the table.

Her shoulders slumped as she raised her head to glare at her husband. "If only you hadn't lost your job. I know it wasn't your fault, it's the pandemic, but dodging these creditors is tough. I'm glad my new job starts next week, though it won't pay much."

Mike stared at her. *Where's the sweet, loving woman I married?* "Look, neither of us signed on for this. At least we have a roof over our head and food on the table. We're lucky Uncle Ralph had this house for us on his acreage."

He turned away and retrieved a flour canister from the cabinet.

"What are you doing? We can't spend any from there, it has to last us until the end of the month." Carol stood to block him from removing money from their hiding place.

He dug through the container. "I'm feeling lucky tonight. I'll just take twenty dollars, there's a lottery ticket with our name on it. I can feel it in my bones."

"No, Mike. We promised we wouldn't play the lottery anymore. Haven't you learned anything these last few months? We need every penny. Please, Mike..." She placed a hand on his arm.

He sighed, then dropped the money back into the canister. "You're right. I know we agreed." He faced her. "I'm looking for a quick fix. I just want us back where we were, financially, emotionally; intimately...I want it all."

"We need to talk with someone. Maybe one of the counselors at church can help us. I meant it when I said I'm in this with you to the end."

"Well, then, why are we arguing?"

Carol reached for his hand. "We both know that one of the major problems in marriages can be finances."

Mike caressed her face. "For tonight, can we put these bills aside and concentrate on us? Please? I need us to be us, the way we used to be."

She gave him a slight smile. "Well, the bills will still be here in the morning. Taking time to focus on us won't make them go away, but it sure couldn't hurt. So, for tonight, no more talking about jobs, money worries or past hurts. This night is for reconnecting with the man I love, I need this, too." She wrapped her arms around his neck and kissed him.

****

Dawn broke...the sun's first rays peeked through the mini blinds. Slender slits and circles of sunlight stretched slowly across the covers of the bed. Mike looked toward the window and sighed.

He'd been awake for hours. A full night of sleep didn't come easily, even though his body was weary after each day of hard labor. Carol stirred beside him, snuggling closer in her own slumber.

He reached for her, finding solace in the closeness they shared. Last night they recaptured some of the feelings from the early days of the marriage. Different, not everything it used to be; harsh words spoken recently still stung.

A chance for a new beginning? He knew they had to get back on the same track. Their life wasn't supposed to be like this. He'd promised her much more than their current circumstances, but he'd failed. This bothered him more than he wanted her to know.

"Morning, Sweetheart," he whispered. He kissed the top of her head. She moved even closer, their bodies nestling in a comfortable familiarity.

"Hmm," she purred, "this is a really nice way to wake up. How long before you have to head to the field?"

"Oh, I've got thirty minutes or so. No time clock to punch here, right?"

"You've been lying awake again, haven't you?" she asked, sitting up to face him. "You don't have to worry about us. I've got the job at the grocery store now. I'm pretty sure that–"

He put his fingers to her lips. "Enough. The job market is what it is. We're lucky my uncle needed help on the farm. I'm just sorry you don't get to finish school. I never meant for you to have to drop out, I–"

"Wait," she kissed his fingers and held his hand to her cheek. "Most important thing is, we're together. We can survive anything."

Mike smiled. "You bet we will. Guess I'd better get up and at 'em. Day isn't gonna get any cooler." He gave her a hug before he climbed out of bed.

Twenty minutes later, she handed him his lunch and a large jug of cold water. "Be careful out there today, the temperature is supposed to be in the high nineties."

"I will. I've only got the west fields to finish plowing. Ralph gave me the weekend off. How about picking up a movie or two for us?"

"I'd like that. Want an action film or a comedy?"

"I think one of each kind. See if they have the latest Star Wars film."

Carol pulled him close. "May God watch over you and help you not be so worried. May we remember our blessings always." She kissed him and watched from the porch as he drove down the dirt lane. She glanced skyward before going back into the house.

****

The drought had been ongoing for weeks, with no relief in sight. Early in the afternoon Mike sat in the shade of the lone tree at the side of the field. Acres and acres of fertile, dusty farmland surrounded him. The nearest house was over a mile away.

He closed his eyes as he leaned against the trunk, appreciative for the slight breeze and looking forward to the weekend.

Moments, or perhaps minutes later his eyes shot open and his hand went instinctively up as something brushed across his face. He pushed whatever touched him into the rough bark. A loud pop startled him even more. He tried to jump to one side until he noticed a balloon.

His heart pounded. In his lap lay an envelope tied with ribbon to the now burst balloon. He picked it up and turned it over. "What's this?"

He read the typed message aloud. "Whoever finds this, please reply to the number inside." He opened the envelope and found a laminated index card with a phone number and the initials, Y.L.D. There were no other clues to tell him who'd launched the balloon or why.

Mike started to wad up the envelope and card but he wanted to show it to Carol, knowing she'd find it interesting. He looked at it again, smoothed it out carefully and put it in his shirt pocket. He rose, packed the remainder of his lunch and climbed back on the tractor to finish plowing.

Late in the afternoon he walked through the kitchen door, dirt and sweat clinging to his brown work shirt and jeans. "Honey, I'm home." She came out of the bathroom, drying her just washed hair with a towel.

"Hi Babe. Thirty minutes until dinner. You've time for a shower."

"Okay. I got the fields ready for planting. Hope there is a forecast change coming."

"Not until next week." She stood in the doorway. "Are you getting used to life as a farmer?"

He faced her and shrugged his shoulders. "It's work. Seems there's no jobs for a draftsman right now." He took a step closer to her, not quite touching so she wouldn't get dirty from his work clothes. He leaned a bit more towards her and inhaled the scent of her shampoo. "We'll be all right. It may take some time, but we'll make it. This is temporary."

Despite the dirt and sweat, Carol rested her head against his chest and wrapped her arms around him. The envelope he'd found earlier was protruding from his pocket a bit and rubbed against her cheek. "What's this?" she asked, pulling it out of his pocket.

He laughed. "That's something that literally landed in my lap today when I was taking a break. I was sitting in the shade with my eyes closed and something brushed against my face. It was a balloon with this envelope attached. I'm not sure what to think about it. I started to throw it away, but I wanted to show it to you first."

She read the card. "I think we should call. Maybe a store of some kind has a prize for whoever finds this. I wonder what Y.L.D. stands for?"

"I don't know. I guess we've nothing to lose."

She handed him his phone, grabbed a pencil from the nightstand and they stood by the edge of the bed as he dialed the number, their heads together as they listened to the speaker. A recording with a man's voice answered.

"Congratulations on finding the balloon. Be at 2224 E California Street, Tulsa, Oklahoma at noon on the first Saturday after you hear this message."

The message was given again and the line went dead. Mike put his phone down. Carol checked what she'd written on the back of the envelope.

"Guess we ought to go see what this is about. How about it, honey? Feel like a trip to town?" he asked her.

"Sure, why not. I've got things I need there, anyway. Don't you think it's kind of weird that a live person didn't answer? What kind of business do you think this is?"

Mike was puzzled. "I'm not sure. Maybe we got the recording 'cuz the business hours are over for the day. Why don't you use Google and see if there's a business or person with that number, address or name? We'll know tomorrow for sure, though."

He began unbuttoning his shirt. "Guess I should take a shower; dinner is about ready, right?"

She giggled as she waved one hand in the air and covered her nose with the other. "A shower would be a great idea; you do smell a bit ripe!"

He laughed, playfully pushed her onto the bed with her towel and went into the bathroom to wash away the day's dirt.

"You know, I like this, I love hearing you laugh again. I think we're going to be okay." He gave her a thumbs up sign before she returned to the dinner preparations.

Mike emerged from the shower, put on some shorts and a tee shirt and went into the kitchen. He snuck up behind her and grabbed her around her waist. She leaned back against him, reaching up with one hand to caress his face.

"You certainly smell better. Are you sure you're my husband?"

He answered by kissing her neck and then her earlobe. "I sure better be if I'm going to take liberties like this..." His voice trailed off as she turned around and they shared a tender kiss. The beeping oven timer interrupted the moment.

"Drat. This is definitely one of those times I didn't want to be saved by the bell."

"Hmm. Me either." She turned off the timer, then pointed to the mysterious card. "Hon, I didn't find any information on Google. Maybe it's a new business. What do you think this is for?"

"Well, hope against hope, maybe someone wants to give us their winning lottery ticket. More than likely, it'll probably be for a tank of gas or a week's worth of groceries. What would you like it to be?"

She put a plate of lasagna in front of him and sat down. "It has to be something big. That balloon could've landed anywhere in the state, so it has to be something big enough to make whoever found it go all the way to Tulsa. For us it's only thirty miles, but that balloon could've made it to Kansas or beyond."

She took a sip of iced tea. "I'm thinking...I'm thinking that it will be something totally unexpected and completely overwhelming."

Mike reached across the table and took her hand in his. "Babe, it would be nice, but we shouldn't get our hopes up. I don't want you to be disappointed. We'd best keep our ideas of this simple, less chance of being hurt that way. Just consider this an adventure, okay?"

"I feel it's going to be a pretty big adventure, and we need to think positive. It was *more* than fate that made that balloon land in your lap. Look at all that empty land it could've landed in and been overlooked? I really believe it'll be something extra good." She squeezed his hand and got up to retrieve her own plate.

The following day they ran some errands in Tulsa, then promptly at noon pulled up to the address she'd written on the envelope. The building had a central lobby with elevators and doors to six offices. There was no mention of a business called Y.L.D. on the tenant directory. Only one door had a light shining thru the window and was slightly ajar. After knocking, a man opened the door.

He nodded and spoke from behind his mask, "Please, follow me." He led them into a large office. "Please, make yourselves comfortable," then he left them alone.

Moments later an elderly man entered. Carol and Mike both stood to greet him. He motioned for them to have a seat as he stood behind the desk.

"I'm good with removing masks if you are, we can do that six-foot spacing pretty easily in this room." He removed his mask, Carol and Mike followed his lead.

He smiled as he spoke. "Very good. You've found the seventh balloon that I released. I received six other phone calls over the last three months, but none of the callers showed up at the appointed time. You're the first ones to go to the trouble to follow up on the instructions."

"Sir," Mike spoke up, "why did you send out the balloons, especially if you didn't get responses from the first six? Why did you keep trying?"

He moved to his chair, sat down and began a slow rocking motion. "Well, son, all worthwhile endeavors take effort and with effort comes rewards. I didn't give up because I believe in the reason behind my launching the balloons." At their look of confusion, he continued. "Let me explain."

The expression on the older man's face changed. For a brief moment he appeared to be sad, but only for a moment. "I'm considered a successful businessman by many. The money I've made in my lifetime was made because I was willing to take chances in my line of work and in my investments.

"When I was a young man, I had a mentor who helped me get my start in business. When I tried to repay him, he requested that I help others throughout my life instead. He felt that was a better return on his money than the money itself. I have tried to do as he asked, and have found I've received many blessings by doing so.

"I was fortunate enough to have a wonderful wife that helped me in the lean years as well as the years of plenty." He picked up a framed photo from the desk and showed it to them.

"This is Adele, my love and my best friend. She had the most important role in my lifetime and now she's waiting for me in heaven." He ran his hand over the photo before setting it back down.

Mike took Carol's hand and squeezed, fully understanding the other man's feelings.

"I truly believe that sharing what I've learned *and* earned over the years have been the reasons I've been successful. I've outlived all of my family. Several charities and my church are provided for in my will. I take great pleasure in giving others help when they least expect it and can appreciate it the most.

"Most of the people that I've shared with never had an idea where their 'boost' came from. I didn't want them to think they owed me something in return for the help. However, they always got a note encouraging them to do for others in ways that they could. The best thanks I could ever receive, and I often did, was seeing many of them passing on their own type of help to others in need.

"I thought I'd put the balloon out there, in the hopes that whoever found it, could use a hand up in some way. I figured the person who actually showed up would be someone who was sure something worthwhile would be waiting for them here."

Mike cleared his throat, "Let me see if I understand you correctly...you planned on getting someone to come here with the idea that they would need help in some way?"

The older gentleman laughed. "Yes, that pretty well sums it up. I put the balloons out there and I figured the good Lord knew who would respond in person.

"I had Harold, the man who let you in, do a cross reference on the phone number you called from. More research was done late last night and early this morning. I know who you are. I know Mike was recently laid off from his job at Wiltech and that Carol would be a senior in college if the funding for school hadn't run out."

Mike shifted in his chair as he realized that this stranger used the internet to learn about them. After all, they had done some digging, too, to find the source of the note. He hadn't considered someone would be checking them out as well.

"Son, you were first in your graduating class and have proved yourself to be an excellent draftsman. Losing your job was a result of the pandemic, not anything that you did wrong. It just so happens, that my businesses are manufacturing and construction and I'm in need of someone with the skills you possess. I spoke with your previous employer; you've got great references. I have a position for you within my company, if you'd like to have it."

Mike was speechless, but only for a moment. A heavy weight lifted from his shoulders. "This is amazing. I'd love to be considered for the position."

The old man turned to Carol. "You were also doing quite well in school when you had to withdraw. I admire folks who want to improve their lives and are willing to work to do so. Whether or not Mike takes a position with the company, I will pick up the tab for the balance of your education and I will also pay off your existing student loans once you have your degree."

Carol began to cry. Mike put his arm around her. There were tears in his eyes, as well. She sobbed several times, exhaled and was finally able to speak. "I don't know what to say. How can we ever thank you? You need to know what a difference finding that balloon is going to make in our lives."

He smiled again and brought his hands together in a clap. "*That* was my whole intent, that someone would have a chance to improve their own life and in turn can improve the opportunities for others for many years after I'm gone. I feel like the right people have stepped forward once again.

"I'd like to get to know you both. I'd like to help you learn how you can share with others in ways that will bless you for a lifetime, as I've been blessed."

"Thank you so much, sir," Mike began, "but we don't even know your name. What does Y.L.D. stand for? We didn't see any such name or business with those initials when we did an internet search."

"Oh, that?" He chuckled. "Those aren't my initials. I'm Winston Hughes, owner and C.E.O of Hughes Enterprises. The Y.L.D. stands for *Your Lucky Day*."

Sidewalk Suspicions

by **Kathlyn Carter Smith**

Stupid restrictions. Stupid pandemic. Just three weeks into this and I need people!

Carly Jackson pulled on her windbreaker and opened the front door of her home. "Well, if we can't use the walking trails around town, I can certainly use the sidewalks in my neighborhood." She didn't know why she said that out loud. There wasn't anyone to hear her grumbling.

Every day since the quarantine-in-place orders were given by the state and local leaders, she'd gone for a walk, once in the morning and again at dusk. As in most larger towns, people went to work, came home, drove into their own garages, and shut the door. Effectively shutting out the people around them, too.

The move to Tulsa in late February came just before the stay-at-home orders. Since then, empty streets and an avoidance of others seemed to be the norm.

She zipped up her jacket over her slender frame. The March winds could still chill a person to the bone. She studied the homes as she walked past them. Her prolific imagination wove life stories about the people behind the brick, wood and stone exteriors.

The house on the corner was a one-story. "Ah, yes, this is the home of Mr. and Mrs. Don't-Come-In-My-Yard." Large landscaping boulders wrapped around the street sides of the property. There were at least three small signs showing a dog squatting within a circle and a line drawn through it. She chuckled. *I wonder what their gripe is? Are they dog haters? Cat lovers?* Several morning papers hadn't been picked up from the front yard. *Do I dare put those on their porch?* She decided not to, and continued her walk.

As she rounded the corner, a car approached. Carly raised her hand, waved, and smiled. A young woman returned her smile and turned at the house on the opposite corner. She got a baby and a toddler out of the back seat and rushed them indoors, out of the cool weather. Stacks of boxes filled up one side of the garage. *Every time I've seen you, it's just been you and the kids. Where's the daddy, Ms. Single Mom? Have you escaped an abusive husband? A jealous boyfriend? Where's your family? Are those kids really yours...or did you kidnap them? Why haven't you unpacked? Are you going to move under the cover of darkness?* Her thoughts ran rampant.

Halfway down the block, she passed a home that had an older Lincoln Continental parked in the open garage, with its hood up. Engine parts were on the ground beside it. This was the ninth different car that had been worked on there since she had moved in. None of them stayed longer than a day. *Mr. Mechanic has another new project. Stolen cars? Grinding off serial numbers? Are you leader of a gang that hijacks people in the dark of night? Do you strip down the cars and sell the parts? Do you leave any witnesses?*

The skies darkened as Carly hurried to finish her walk, wanting to put some distance between her and the sinister mechanic. As she passed the Don't-Come-in-My-Yard neighbor, she decided to take a chance and grabbed the papers off the lawn. She rang the doorbell and stepped back to the edge of the porch.

The door opened just a crack and the left half of a face peered through the opening. The chain lock on the door was secured. "Who are you? What do you want?"

Carly stiffened. That was not the greeting she expected. She forced a smile. "Hi. I'm Carly Jackson. I just moved in down the street, and I noticed you hadn't picked up your newspapers, so I thought I'd bring them to your door before the storm gets here." *This was a waste of time. How unfriendly can they be?* "Let me just put them on the chair and you can get them after I leave."

She put the papers down and started to turn away. "Wait, I'm sorry. I thought you were selling something. Thank you, it's Carly, right?"

The person behind the door opened it a bit wider, but didn't unlock the chain. Carly caught a glimpse of a frail-looking woman. Her heart softened. *She reminds me of my grandma.*

"Did you buy the Carter's house? My husband and I live here. I'm Ella. We don't get out too much, especially now, with this virus thing happening. That, and neither of us are as sure-footed as we used to be."

"I'm very pleased to meet you, Ella. How about if I put your newspaper on your front porch in the mornings when I take my walk? Would that be helpful for you?"

Ella smiled. "Why, my dear, that would be lovely. My Von has missed those crossword puzzles." She winked. "I kinda like the Sudoku myself." She didn't unlock the chain, but her demeanor definitely changed. Carly understood her caution about a stranger at the door. Maybe a few paper deliveries would gain Ella's trust.

Big raindrops started to splat on the sidewalk as a flash of lightning and a resounding boom shook the ground. Both women flinched at the sound. "I'd better run, I'll have your paper on the porch in the morning." Carly waved, turned, and sprinted to her home, reaching her porch just as the deluge hit.

As promised, she put the newspaper on the chair by Ella's front door every morning. Mr. Mechanic's latest steal disappeared the same afternoon she saw it. Two days later, a fifties Plymouth with the fins on the back had taken its place. *I wonder why he steals older cars? Do people not miss them as much? Or is the market for older cars greater? That one has to be a gas guzzler.*

Her afternoon walk happened a bit earlier in the day, and she was surprised to see Mr. Mechanic on his driveway, talking to an older couple. Curious, she stopped on the sidewalk beside a small hedge, under the premise of tying her shoes, and listened to the conversation. They were speaking louder than normal. Maybe it was the distance thing making them do so, or they were compensating because of the masks the seniors were wearing.

"Nick, are you sure we can't pay you for the oil change and tire rotation? At least a little something?" The older gentleman reached for his wallet in his pants pocket.

Nick (aka Mr. Mechanic) laughed and opened the passenger door for the woman. "It's my pleasure, Carl. You just see that Adele gets home safe and sound. And Adele, those chocolate chip cookies are all the payment I need." He closed the door and watched as the couple backed out of the driveway. Carly stood and turned to continue her walk.

His deep voice stopped her in her tracks. "Hi. Enjoying the day?"

Startled, she stammered, "Oh, me? Yes, hmm, I go out every day in the neighborhood." *Oh my gosh, I'm babbling.*

"I know. I've seen you." He watched her intently. *Those blue eyes...wow!*

Her nerves got the best of her. Without thinking, she blurted out, "You've had so many different cars parked here, I thought you were a car thief..." *Drat, why did I open my big mouth?*

He looked surprised. "A car thief?" He laughed.

She grinned sheepishly. "Well, in my mind, that's what I figured your profession was. Though, to be honest, I didn't know why all the cars were older models and not fancy new ones."

He laughed. "Trust me, miss, if I were going to steal cars, they wouldn't be the ones you've seen here. You must be the person who bought the Carter's home. Have you had time to get settled in? By the way, I'm Nicholas Ford. My friends call me Nick."

Carly sighed. "I'm Carly Jackson, originally from Dallas. I've had nothing but time, so I'm very settled in. I'd shake your hand, but not supposed to. HomeTech Properties offered me a job in Tulsa, but we're all working from our own homes right now."

"Yeah, me, too. Happening all over the country. It has allowed me some extra time to help with the car maintenance for some church members, like the elderly folks who still drive, and some of the single parents."

Hmm, Mr. Nice Guy, and he attends church. She smiled at him. "They seem to appreciate you. What's your other job?"

Nick tossed the greasy towel he used onto a pile at the corner of the garage. "I'm owner of the oldest and largest swim instruction schools in Oklahoma. I also coach competitive swim teams. With this pandemic, our activities have been suspended, so I've got plenty of time, too." He pointed across the street. "I noticed you've been putting the morning paper on Ella and Von's porch."

He grabbed his jacket from a hook next to the garage door and slipped it on over his form fitting tee shirt. *A swimmer? No wonder he looks so fit!*

Carly leaned against the tree next to his driveway. "Seems like they can't get out as easily, and I enjoy visiting when she opens the door. She actually unlocked the chain this morning. Guess she figured out that I'm not a threat. What's the deal with the big rocks in their yard? No other home around here has those."

He ran his hand through his hair and frowned. "Last summer some kids drove their cars through their yard as a shortcut around the corner."

"Oh, that explains a lot. What about the anti-dog signs? Do they hate dogs?"

Nick laughed. "No, but they don't like the mess the dogs leave and the owners who don't pick up after them. As you can imagine, they can't easily clean up after dogs."

She nodded in agreement. "So, Nick, how long have you lived here?"

"Well, I've been here three years. I spent several years after college working to qualify for the U.S. Olympic team. Almost made it. The opportunity to purchase the school came up and I had to think long term."

"Do people ever come outdoors?"

"There will be more neighbors out once the weather warms up. People have a tendency to stay indoors during the winter months or the rainy season. In fact, we have a neighborhood garage sale in June, a July 4th fireworks watch party, and usually something during the fall. We're not a big neighborhood, but most folks are pretty friendly."

Carly smiled. That was good to know. She glanced at her watch and down the street. "Guess I should finish my walk. Nice meeting you, Nick."

"Nice meeting you, too, Carly. Enjoy your walk. I'll be seeing you."

She took a few steps away and glanced over her shoulder. He gave her a grin and a small wave. She felt a warm flush rise to her cheeks as she waved back. He couldn't see the smile on her face as she walked away. *Interesting man. My first guy friend in Tulsa.* Her pace quickened to match her heartbeat.

****

Carly's walks took her by the single mom's house both coming and going. On an afternoon four days after meeting Nick, the woman pulled in the drive, opened the garage door, and unloaded the children and some groceries as Carly passed.

"Looks like you have your hands full. Would you like some help?" Carly paused as she asked. She pulled up the mask from around her neck before stepping closer.

"What? Oh, yes, they are a handful. I'm used to it, thank you."

She introduced herself. "I live in the pinkish brick house, and I'm trying to meet some neighbors. Are you new here, too? I noticed all the boxes." She gave a nod toward the garage.

The young woman swayed as she held the stirring baby and grasped the toddler's hand. "I'm Amy. I just don't seem to have time or energy to unpack. I work, have the kids to corral, and wake up and do it all again. My husband is deployed with the Air Force."

She's a military wife! That explains not seeing a man around. "What a great thing for him to do. That takes a special love of country. I don't think many people realize how it affects the whole family. My thanks to both of you for his service."

Amy smiled. "I'm very proud of him. When he returns stateside next month his enlistment period will be over, and we're settling here in Tulsa. I just can't seem to get everything done on my own."

"I'd be happy to help you. I'm pretty strong and kids love me. I haven't been around anyone to be exposed to this virus, so you don't have to worry on that front. Would you like some help?"

Amy's face lit up with a bright smile. "Oh, my goodness, you don't know how much that means to me. Yes, I'd love some help. And even more, I'd love having a new friend. Thank you! Right now, I need to get these two inside, fed, and to bed. Would tomorrow evening work? About seven-thirty? The kids will be asleep."

It was Carly's turn to smile. "You bet; I'll see you then. Here, let me get these sacks to your door for you." She followed Amy to her door and set the groceries on the floor.

"Thank you so much. Really nice meeting you." Carly walked out to the sidewalk as the garage door closed. She hummed a little tune and continued her walk. There was a spring in her step. *Three mystery homes aren't a mystery anymore. I think I like living here!*

****

The weather warmed up, and the spring days brought people outside just as Nick had predicted. Carly met more neighbors, from a distance, of course. She continued to get the newspapers for Von and Ella and even enjoyed morning coffee with them on their patio on several occasions. Nick helped her with a dead battery one morning and they developed a friendship that involved take-out dinners and long talks on one of their driveways. With Carly's help, Amy got the moving boxes unpacked and her house truly became a home for her young family. As the weeks passed, their friendship grew stronger. They exchanged house keys and emergency contacts. Several times Carly watched the children so Amy could run errands without them in tow.

Soon it was time for Amy's husband, Paul, to arrive home, and Carly had a surprise in store for them.

It was early evening as the couple turned onto their street from the airport. They were greeted with a whole block of neighbors waving American flags. Many held signs that said, "Welcome home" or, "Thank you for your service." Von and Ella sat in folding chairs on their driveway. They hadn't wanted to miss the homecoming.

There were cheers and applause as Paul stepped out of the van. Paul and Amy each held one of their children as they greeted the neighborhood. Amy's tears were matched by many of the neighbors. Carly stepped forward, lowered her mask and spoke into a bullhorn. "Friends, today we get to honor and thank Paul Thompson for his service and sacrifice as he served in the United States Air Force for the past four years. We also thank his wife, Amy, for keeping the home fires burning as she anxiously waited for today to happen. Amy and Paul, inside your home there's a catered meal provided by Mitchell's Steak House. There's also a card on the table with a Visa Gift Card from all of us here. Welcome home!"

Another round of cheers followed and the neighbors slowly returned to their own homes. Nick and Carly visited with the reunited couple for another few minutes before saying goodnight.

When they stepped off the curb to head to Carly's house, Nick spoke first. "That was a lovely thing for you to do. Thank you for organizing all of this." He took her hand in his as they continued across the street.

Carly's heart rate sped up at his touch. The friendship held such promise, and apparently, Nick felt the same way. "It was my pleasure. This has been a crazy time in our town, our world. Being grateful, well, it just seems more important than ever to share that feeling." She looked up at him.

He stopped her on the sidewalk and let go of her hand as he used both hands to lower his mask, then hers. "I'm thankful that we've had time to get to know each other. I would like to see where this friendship leads. Would that be okay with you?"

Carly's smile was all the answer he needed as he leaned in to share a tender kiss. When they finally broke apart, he said, "This pandemic has brought chaos, but it also brought you into my life. To think that it all started with you suspecting I was a car thief."

She chuckled. "My silly imagination...I've never been so glad that I was so wrong." She kissed him again, grateful for the moment and the promise of a bright future.

KATHLYN CARTER SMITH

Kathlyn Carter Smith is an award-winning author, realtor, golfer, OK State sports fan and mom living in Broken Arrow, OK. Much of her writing touches on how God works in her character's lives, just as He has worked in hers. Romantic themes & happily-ever-afters fit her optimistic outlook on life.

Dark Passage

by **Carol Lavelle Snow**

our guide turns out the lights
and we stand very still

soft sound of water
dripping
faint mechanical sound
far behind us
an elevator
coming to a stop

someone sighs
then quiet

blackness closes in

I could reach out
touch the cold metal rail
beside me
use it to steady myself
even use it to follow the path
to the top
if I had to

but we're tourists
we won't be left in the dark
everything will be clear

someday

CAROL LAVELLE SNOW

•●•

Carol Lavelle Snow is a former college English instructor who has written for the Narrative Television Network and Spotlight Theater. She appeared as Aunt Eller in Discoveryland's production of *Oklahoma!* for 11 summers. She has published fiction as well as poetry—in magazines including *Harp-Strings Poetry Journal*, *StepAway Magazine*, and *The Lyric*.

COVID-19 Lament

by M. Carolyn Steele

I've been sitting here with my coffee, watching the birds outside the window keep their social distance, and chatting with the plants about people going off the deep end with this self-isolation business. The stress is definitely affecting Ivy, causing her to go to vine. It concerns me. Her leaves are beginning to turn a sickly yellow. The philodendron keeps wanting another drink. I hope poor Phil doesn't need AA before this COVID stuff is over.

It's no use trying to discuss the virus with Buddy, my computer. When I try to tell him about the latest safety rituals, he insists on shutting down. He's been temperamental ever since he came into this house. I'm fed up and tempted to give him the boot.

In fact, I was talking about that very thing with the coffee pot this morning. I didn't get far, however. Her mood has been dark here lately, and the fridge is no help. He's giving me the cold shoulder, humming away in that low, monotonous tune. I'm thinking something might be brewing between the two of them. When I urge him to talk, he completely freezes up.

Tootsie Toaster isn't much company, always popping up with some new CDC statistic. I tell her to stop it. She's depressing the dryer. He's been spinning out of control with worry the past few days and doesn't know when to shut down.

Goodness, it's easy during this pandemic to get the stove fired up. He is hateful and makes it his mission to scorch everything that comes near. Tilly Teapot doesn't make matters any better. She's constantly blowing off steam about the latest shortages at the grocery store. In fact, there's endless bickering in the kitchen with Freddie Fry Pan trying to convince us that his Teflon coating makes him immune to the infection.

Swept up in conspiracy theories, Betty Broom is terrified and isolates in the closet, refusing to come out. Molly Mop, on the other hand, thinks the entire situation is over-blown and our ideas are all wet. If she would wear her mask on a regular basis, I wouldn't dip her head in soapy water to get rid of those nasty germs.

As soon as the quarantine is lifted, I'm going to take my cell phone to the dentist to get his blue tooth checked. As for Lucy Land Line, she has become a real ding-a-ling since the doorbell went silent.

If this pandemic drags on much longer, I think I'll get a parrot just so I have someone sensible to talk to.

The Faceless Ones of Site 013

by **M. Carolyn Steele**

"Indeed, it looks like we have another pannie pit." Professor Balthus pointed to the tally wall just inside the cave entrance.

A groan worked its way up my throat, but I swallowed it. As the newest and youngest on the team, I was expected to be excited no matter what was found. I could have told the professor it was another one just by the smell. Especially strong, the centuries hadn't diluted the heavy, musty odor of fear and death one iota.

"This one wasn't on the map. How did you find it?"

"A feeling, a hunch, just something." Balthus looked toward me, rattling the collection of hand shovels, small picks, and brushes dangling from his backpack as it slipped from his shoulders. "How many does that make now, Lyra?"

With a silent sigh, I settled my equipment on the ground, squatted and fished my notebook out. Flipping pages, I scanned entries I'd made for the past year. "Um…thirteen, just on this ridge, sir."

"Very well, designate this site, 013." Armed with a shovel, Balthus touched the flashlight sewn to the broad collar on his jacket, turned and followed the beam into the cave's shadows. His voice deepened in the vastness of the space and traveled back, "With, you know, the usual prefix."

Relaxing against the limestone wall, I reviewed entries with nearly the same information, and then entered the new data. Date: 24 Sept 2220, Old West Virginia, Rattlesnake Ridge, Site 013. Entrance: 3 bods wide, 2 bods high. Dense growth.

I looked from my notes to study the scrub trees, hackberry and the like, nearly blocking the cave opening. At that instant, Lipton Adams fought a twisting swag of vines and pushed his way through the tangle into the cave accompanied by his own brand of frustration.

"Of all the crooked, piss-poor jobs of clearing the path." Lippy jerked a dried twig from his mass of auburn hair and snapped it with one hand. "Who cleared that?" He arched his back, grumbling as his pack slid to the ground.

"Professor Balthus did. Another one of his hunches. This cave isn't on the map and he didn't want to wait for site clearing. We barely squeezed through."

"Thanks for tying your head scarf out there. Probably would have hiked past that turn off."

"Yeah. Afraid you would, Lippy." I stretched for the pink bandana he dangled just out of reach.

"I like your hair undone better. It's golden when the sun catches it." His grin was the nicest thing about this assignment – bright, honest, irresistible.

"Um-hum. Well, the sun won't catch it in here." I snatched the bandana. "Now, break out the signage. We need this site marked before the professor gets back, in case he wants to do some digging."

Lippy tugged at the buckles of his pack and unloaded a small white sign. He nodded toward the tally wall. "Have you counted the number of faceless ones yet?"

I shook my head and studied the pattern of finger-length lines, all in straight rows, beginning head high, carved across the cave surface, top to bottom. Each mark represented five bodies, not one. Since the beginning, burials seldom matched numbers on the walls. There were usually more bodies than recorded.

"Why don't you count 'em?" I balanced the sign on one knee, shook a bottle of reflective paint, and printed in block letters. OWV, RR, 013. Printing was a lost art. That I could read and write cursive made me valuable to old Balthus. He didn't trust electronics since the problems after the COVID-19 pandemic, always wanted a back-up.

And I was the back-up. Just once I'd like to discover a written journal instead of long dead, cracked communication devices. No battery yet invented could last 200 years.

A heavy thud from the cave's interior, followed by the clack and tumble of disturbed rocks echoing in the stillness, brought a whiff of stale air. Sometimes the professor was like a bull doing the two-step in a china closet. I attached the sign to a metal stand and leaned it against the wall.

Behind me, Lippy's mumbling was somehow comforting in this cave of the dead. He counted off groupings of one-hundred and marked them with yellow chalk. When I accepted the internship, I didn't expect to be assigned to the COVID-19 surveys. No one found anything in these digs. People quit wearing adornments at the beginning of the troubles when it was found the virus hid in ring mountings and scroll work. And the haste necessary as deaths multiplied prohibited ceremony – each poor soul went to his communal grave with only a body bag, old or young, male or female.

"I count 455." Lippy sat on his heels and flipped his collar light on. "Funny thing. The last three markings get shallow, untidy, and then," he pointed at the wall, "what do you make of this?"

"Just a minute." I tilted my notebook toward the entrance for better light to record notes. "We're going to have to pull away more foliage or it'll be pitch black soon." Thick vines swayed in the small opening we'd made, causing narrow shafts of daylight to shudder off and on.

Joining Lippy, I bent close to the cave's surface and gently swept over faint marks with my brush to loosen centuries of dust. "AL S LST. I believe it's twenty-first century shorthand. You know, when people messaged back and forth on cell phones instead of speaking with each other."

"Yeah? Someone's name, maybe? If this site wasn't on the map, then there probably aren't any records of who was interred here."

"No, not a name. It's a message, I think." I sat back and stared at the crude letters, hugging myself against a sudden realization. "All is lost."

"What?" Lippy drew the question out, voice low, hoarse. His eyes disappeared into dark sockets as light from his collar illuminated his chin and nose. He reached to flip on my light and I knew I appeared just as ghoulish.

"Strange message to leave," he said.

"Maybe someone got left behind. I imagine the last one in this part of the country felt like it was the end of the world. Everything failing, no communication, no supplies, half the world's population vanished."

I glanced over my shoulder at the entrance and watched as one by one, pin holes of light shut off, sudden darkness making the sour air seem thick. Lippy turned around, his light illuminating the blanket of greenery with its tightly woven twists of branches and vines. He helped me to my feet.

"Get a pick. We better open up the entrance." He slid a short-bladed machete from his backpack and swung at a vine thick as a man's arm. The mat of vegetation quivered, loosening a shower of twigs and golden leaves, but the blade barely made a dent. The vine held. A rush of small flying insects buzzed toward our lights, their wings green and luminous. We batted the air and they were gone into the darkness.

"What were those?" I asked, shaking the front of my shirt, glad for the bandana's protection.

"Blasted bugs. Hate 'em," Lippy muttered and brushed through his hair.

"Let me have a try with the pick," I said and balanced my weight for the effort. The pick pierced the obstinate vine with a liquid slush and stayed put despite my attempts at removal. "It won't come out."

"Trade." Lippy handed me the machete. "If we can get this big one broken, maybe it will all open up." He grunted with the attempt to twist the pick back and forth. Slime oozed from the wound, inched down the thick stalk catching leaves as it went.

"That stuff is like glue." Lippy wiped his hands on his pants and stepped back to survey the overgrown entrance. "Maybe, try the smaller ones."

Thin vines groped toward me, fluttering, almost dodging as I chopped at dozens of shoots. The bushes rustled softly, like a muffled groan. I bent to the task of clearing a spot big enough to reach in, and grab a mottled tree branch.

The brush against my flesh was soft at first, feathery, as something circled my arm. I released the branch and tried to back away, but the grip intensified driving my wrist phone into my flesh, hurting.

"Help me, Lippy." A wave of panic charged through me and I fought the urge to scream. "I'm caught."

Lippy grasped my arm and pulled, bringing a speckled vine along. He grabbed the machete, hacking until the vine loosened and retracted into the thicket taking my phone with it.

"It let us in, but won't let us out," he said. "You okay, Lyra?"

I nodded, flexing my fingers. A red welp circled my throbbing wrist. Bumps and bruises were common on digs, but this was different. My breath came in ragged gulps. "I...I was never good at gardening."

"Some garden." Lippy smiled, a thin sympathetic grin. "That was scary, I know."

"This survey is on such a budget. The professor will be mad I lost my communication."

"We'll get it back." Lippy handed my pack over, then shrugged into his and picked up the professor's. "I wonder were Balthus is? I hope he remembered to charge the energy packs. We'll need to contact a team with a laser to get through that jungle."

We stood a minute, staring at the embedded tool that defied removal, then both turned toward the cave interior. Our lights sliced through the gloomy darkness, growing softer in the distance. Deeper, the walls turned craggy, with indentations and holes marring the surface.

"There," Lippy motioned to the ground. "The professor's footprints." He adjusted his collar so the beam illuminated the prints as they rounded a curve.

"Wait," I grabbed Lippy's arm before he could make the turn and pointed at the wall ahead. Lines, faint, different from the natural swirls of rock came to life as we walked closer. Dust, undisturbed for ages, rose in puffs speckling our light beams as slowly, a myriad of drawings took shape. I leaned close and noted crude brush strokes, likely made with wet charcoal ashes.

"Mississippian culture?" Lippy squinted at two upright figures, blank outlines with no detail. "Typical faceless ones. And, there," he pointed to another drawing, a long-billed bird, wings in flight.

"Probably a woodpecker. Some early tribes believed the woodpecker guided the soul to the after-world." At last, something exciting. I resisted touching my finger to the wall. "The professor says we walk on the bones of our ancestors. Stands to reason these caves were used in earliest America before they became dumping grounds for the Wuhan dead."

"Nice of the ancient spirits to share their cave," Lippy muttered.

"Not happily, I'd imagine. All those jagged lines above the woodpecker represent lightning marks, believed to be a symbol of evil demons." I studied the wall. "Something awful must have happened here."

Lippy dug in his backpack for a hand-held, flipped the lever to spotlight, and trained it on the blackened ceiling. "See the soot. We dig, we'll find campfire remnants." He backed away from the wall, sweeping the surrounding ground for a tell.

"What have we here?" Lippy motioned toward a partially buried canvas bag.

I squatted and gently scooped a handful of dirt aside, uncovering the metal clasps. Did I dare lift the flap? The heavy cloth felt rough to my fingers, but not fragile.

"Sometimes textiles survive for centuries depending on the climate. Best wait for the professor. Wonder who it belonged to?"

Lippy nudged me, jerking his thumb over his shoulder, and half-whispered. "I imagine him."

A sharp intake of air brought with it the taste of mold and dust, a taste of the ages. I steadied my breathing, willed the creep of flesh along my arms to still. A few feet away, a skeleton took shape in Lippy's spotlight beam, bringing to life the dull glare of bones.

Tattered shreds of cloth hung suspended from an ulna bone leaning against the wall, and fluttered with our movements as if waving, trying to catch our attention. On the ground, curved ribs rested atop the snake of spinal vertebrae that disappeared beneath what was left of pant remnants exposing femur and tibia bones.

We crouched to stare at the skull gaping back at us, the interior visible through vacant eye sockets. Adult. Most likely a male from all appearances.

"Lower jaw dropped away from the upper. Had good teeth, though." Lippy nudged my shoulder with his. "You're trembling. You scared of a few bones?"

"Of course not." I shook my head. "It's just finding them naked like this and not buried…seems weird. If this is a COVID-19 victim, why is it out here and not in the pit?"

"Good question."

I rummaged in my backpack for the IRD camera. No need for a

light source with that baby. "The professor will want pictures in situ before we examine anything. I wonder where he is."

We turned toward the direction Professor Balthus took. Lippy stood. "Guess I better locate him. You photo catalog the find and keep our new friend company." He left, taking the spotlight with him.

Clicking away, I documented every angle of my silent friend stretched out against the wall, the collection of phalange bones that tumbled one by one from its upright arm as skin and muscle and ligament decomposed, pearlized buttons keeping company with the spine, and cracked leather boots containing what was left of the feet.

The skeleton appeared to be complete, and as I looked closer, hadn't been disturbed by animals. No surprise. A year into the troubles, dogs, cats, and the like, whether wild or domestic, began succumbing.

"Mac," I said, my voice hollow in the cavern. "You look like a Mac. How did you get yourself in this fix?" The canvas bag was within reaching distance for all the good it did him. Backing up, to get a wide shot of the cave drawings, I stumbled into a ring of small stones, its contents crunching under my weight.

"Oh damn, Mac. Looks like you made yourself at home and I stepped right in it." I dropped to one knee. Charred lumps nestled in blackened flakes that crumbled when touched.

Why build a fire? Since the pandemic, fear of a virus that refused to die had restricted camping in this part of the country. Whole forests were burned once it was discovered COVID-19 could harbor in a tree's rough bark. Trees like oak, maple...even, hackberry. My wrist ached anew with the thought of something impossible.

"No," I whispered as if afraid of disturbing Mac's slumber. "Can't be." I stood, adjusted my collar light to focus on the entrance. Movement, slight, trembling, rustled the foliage in soft sighs.

"I'll just go find the others," I spoke into the darkness and turned, determined not to run, not to be panicked. The cave narrowed, ceiling lowered as I followed Balthus and Lippy's footsteps to a dead-end. A stone wall, obviously man-made, blocked further passage yet I could hear the drone of conversation.

"Lippy? Professor?" My voice bounced back at me, high-pitched, wobbly.

"Over here," Lippy flashed his light from the edge of the wall. "You'll have to climb through."

Waist high, rocks had been removed leaving room for a person to squeeze into the next cavern. I hefted myself up, threw both legs over the barrier, then slid down into Lippy's arms. For a minute I didn't want to let go. Being alone with Mac had unnerved me. Silly.

"Hey, everything all right?" Lippy drew back and smiled.

"Lyra, glad you're here." Professor Balthus interrupted, his eyes wide, excited. He waved toward a massive pit behind him, centuries of settling making the boundary obvious. "You need to document this, especially these bodies here."

"Thanks," I said to Lippy and released my hold on his shoulders. Glad I'd not left the camera behind, I turned to the professor, who hurried me to the edge of the pit.

"Why aren't they in body bags?" I stared down at three skeletons, and despite a layer of dust could tell their clothing was as disintegrated as Mac's.

"Obviously, placed after the burials were complete." Balthus rubbed his hands together. "Found another two pits at the back of the cave."

I focused the camera on the group of three. They'd been dumped one atop the other. It would be a chore to separate the bones.

"Finished?" The professor patted my shoulder. "Now, let's take a look at that pouch you two found." We clambered back through the opening, dislodging rocks in the process.

"Why'd they wall up the pits?" I huffed, keeping pace with Balthus' long strides. "It wasn't as if they kept them secret."

"Never been done before." The professor squatted next to the bag, unhooking the clasps to peer inside. "This is a surprise."

"What?" Lippy and I both said, kneeling as the professor removed a small bound packet of paper and held it in the flat of his hand.

"Twenty-first century currency. First National Bank, Boston, by the money band. We've been using credits for a hundred years now."

"Real money?" I held open a specimen bag. "I've only seen pictures."

The professor nodded. "Hundred-dollar increments. I've seen twenty-dollar bills my ancestors didn't turn in. Appears to be more."

"We'll have to research unsolved crimes when we get back to camp." Lippy coughed, the sound startling in the confines.

"You think this is a crime?" I watched as the professor tapped his chin.

"Yes, a robbery. Think about it. Where better to hide a theft than a pannie cave? It would be safe, no one wanting to venture near the mass burials." Balthus glanced into the darkness. "Wall the burials off for good measure. Come back a year or two later."

"Oh, Mac." I turned toward the skeleton leaned against the cave wall. "You were nothing more than a thief."

"Mac?" Lippy and the professor stared at me.

"Yeah, him, over there. Why is he here, while the others are in the pit? Think he killed them? Then, for some reason, didn't leave?"

"I didn't note signs of violence." The professor cleared his throat and poked into the bag again. "We'll know more back at the laboratory."

"Maybe, he couldn't leave." Lippy swung his spotlight toward the entrance, and aimed it on the pick. Whatever seeped from the vine now pooled on the ground.

"Perhaps, this will tell us." Balthus held up a small booklet that fell open in his hands. "Cursive. Do the honors, Lyra."

The faded leather binding held a story – words from the past. I took a deep breath stirring a tickle in my throat.

"This 3-ring binder is smaller than most." I adjusted my collar light on the yellowed pages and sighed. "They used pencil which fades over time." Leaning closer, its aged odor wafted up. "Numbers. Possibly longitude and latitude? Looks like old-style directions. Highway 56, north Pikeville, ridge trail."

"Ruins of Pikeville, maybe 50 miles, I think." The professor tapped the screen on his mapping instrument. "Anyone bring batteries?"

Lippy looked at me and rolled his eyes.

I gently turned the pages and continued, "Appears to be lists of supplies. Oh, here, different handwriting…Jimmy and Alex took sick, fever, cough. Where's Brad with the copter?"

"Fever?" Lippy gestured toward the pits. "Suppose they came down with the virus?"

"Maybe. Like the great plagues of the past, the Wuhan virus raged for several years." The professor frowned. "Go on."

"Now someone else writes, see the slant, left-handed most likely. Says… hauled Jim and Alex to pits. Supplies low. No medicine. Irv sick…jokes about two-way split if helicopter doesn't show."

Despite everyone's light illuminating the page, the writing became harder to read. "Pencil lost its point. Lines are fainter. We'll need the spectrolight to bring some of this up, but here I can make out….to the pit. And, here…damn cave, sick, need hatchet, can't get out." I sat back and studied the skeleton. "Something got Mac, too."

Question was, what? A disease believed eradicated two-hundred years ago—or, I glanced up at the lightning bolts raining across the wall—a cave of evil spirits?

Lippy trained his spotlight on the tangled entrance again, catching the glitter of luminous insects in the beam. "I'd say now is the time to contact help."

"How will they know where we are?" I asked, thinking about my wrist phone gobbled by the vines. "This isn't on the map."

"No worry. They'll triangulate from our signal." The professor stifled a cough, then pulled out his communication device, and flipped it on. "Balthus here. Need laser team to extract us from unmarked site on Rattlesnake Ridge."

The screen flashed with color and fluttered, went gray, then blank, leaving a coarse hiss that sputtered and faded away.

M. CAROLYN STEELE

M. Carolyn Steele retired from a commercial art career to pursue a love of writing. Historical eras, specifically Civil War and Native American, capture her imagination. Nominated for a Pushcart Prize, she has won numerous writing awards including several crème-de-la-creme, and is published in seventeen anthologies. A Native American historical novel, *Spirit of the Crow*, was released in 2017 and a Civil War novel, *Outrun the Bullets*, is an August 2019 release. Combining her knowledge of storytelling and genealogy, she presents programs designed to inspire others to record their own family stories. She authored the book, *Preserving Family Legends for Future Generations*, a 2010 Heartland New Day Bookfest First Place winner.

Website: www.mcarolynsteele.com.

Total Warfare Before Breakfast

by **Beverly Strader**

COVID-19 supply disruptions kept our regular grocery store from stocking Total, my husband's favorite breakfast cereal. Being a mostly considerate wife, I set forth on a noble quest to bring home this suddenly rare commodity. My search took me to a major chain store that I will not name here, but the name begins with W and ends with T.

Early in the morning I went, hoping to avoid the virus and get home in time for breakfast. I scanned the many offerings in the cereal section, once, twice, three times.

There it was. I spotted that lonely, only box way up high, on the very top shelf. My prize in sight, I went looking for a helpful employee to get it down, but I seemed to be totally alone in that store.

Plan B: I tested the shelves, but they were designed to hold cereal, not support short senior citizens on mighty quests. Climbing up to the cereal was clearly not an option. Time for Plan C.

At the far end of the aisle was the toy section, right next to the sugarcoated superhero cereals. On display, in easy reach of shorter folks, stood a box of light sabers. *Of course, use the Force!* I pulled one from the display. Apparently light sabers were motion activated. I marched on to face my quarry with lights flashing and full sound effects. Total domination!

I leaped into action, thrusting the mighty beeping, blinking weapon high over my head. I hit my target, but the box fell backward. I jumped up and parried to the side, sliding it forward just a bit. I battled the box to the edge of the shelf. Channeling the Force with all my being, I jumped as high as I could, swinging the light saber Obe Wan Kenobi-style.

Success! I caught the airborne box of cereal with my free hand. Light saber held high in triumph, I congratulated myself with a hearty, "Yesss!" Then I heard applause behind me in the now crowded cereal aisle. So much for social distancing…

In for a penny, in for a pound, I turned and bowed to my audience. If I was going to end up on Facebook, I would do it with panache. Maybe I'd go viral?

I marched majorette-style, brandishing the still beeping, blinking weapon back to the display at the end of the aisle. I returned the toy to its box with enough Force to awaken all the other light sabers. With this glorious chorus behind me, I hit the self-checkout and drove straight home in time for breakfast.

I forgot to get milk.

BEVERLY STRADER

Beverly Strader is a proud "Okie from Kentucky". She is a lifelong storyteller and has received awards from OWFI and The Tulsa City County Library. A Tulsan since 1979, she and her husband live in Midtown.

Delivering Dreams

by **Linda Trout**

A ngela Broadhurst pushed off with her foot, keeping the porch swing moving at a slow, steady pace. A gentle breeze fluttered her hair and swayed the newly budded leaves on the elm trees. The grass was more green than brown, and the air no longer held a chill.

Spring had burst forth like a Monet painting.

A cloud of dust kicked up as the engine grind of the Express Delivery Service truck reached her ears. Would it turn in her drive today or go on to one of the neighbors? To her delight, the truck pulled in. She'd forgotten what she'd ordered last. It didn't matter. Opening the box to see whatever treasure it held was always exciting.

She waited as the delivery truck came to a stop. She'd gotten to know the driver, Ralph, over the last couple of months, and would welcome the few moments of human contact before he left to make his next stop.

Except, the man who jumped down was pretty much the opposite of Ralph. Tall, slim, and with a full head of brown hair, she raised her eyebrows in appreciation, wishing for a split second that he wasn't wearing a mask so she could see the rest of his face.

She didn't want to startle him, but wanted to say *something*. After all, he was the first person she'd seen in days and couldn't pass up the opportunity. "You're new."

He jerked around and faced her. Eyes wide, he said, "S-sorry. D-didn't see you there."

Making a point of holding up the box—hmm, no wedding ring—he placed the package on the bench next to the door. She caught his subtle perusal of her before turning to go.

"Thank you for the delivery. You have a good day, okay?"

He gave her a short nod before continuing down the walk. *Are you substituting, or will I be seeing more of you?* she wondered. The latter, she hoped as she watched his easy, confident stride. Maybe next time he could stay for a few minutes and talk. It had been a long time since she'd visited with anyone in person.

After working in advertising for a number of years on both coasts, she had sold her New York City flat and moved back to Oklahoma three months earlier. The sale gave her enough money to purchase a home, with enough cash left over to allow time to decide what to do next.

The white clapboard house with a wraparound porch was perfect. After years of living in crowded cities, Angela simply wanted to be left alone and she didn't bother meeting any of the neighbors on the rural road...the quiet and solitude being everything she dreamed about. Until the pandemic hit. Then, because there were orders to stay at home, she wanted to go places.

To do things.

To see people.

Of course, that didn't happen. Staying home was the logical option, the best option. Being young and healthy didn't mean she wouldn't be affected by the virus that had rapidly overtaken the entire world.

Still, she sometimes craved the noisy and hectic city, and even the friends she'd cut out of her life. She kept turning down their invitations until they finally stopped asking. Now, she felt bad about how she'd left things and worried about their safety. She made a mental note to call her best friend, Sue, to see how she was coping. Although, with the way the virus had shut down everything in the city, Angela was glad she was already gone.

Hours later, while working in the neglected and overgrown flower bed, she kept thinking about the cute deliveryman. If he was the new driver, she intended to see more of him. Time to hit the online nursery sites. Adding some decorations to her sparsely furnished house wouldn't hurt, either.

****

Jon Fischer couldn't stop thinking about the beautiful woman at his mid-morning delivery. Her wheat-colored hair had glistened in the sunlight, highlighting her pretty smile and fair skin. Mentally shaking himself, he refocused on the job. Getting fired the first week wouldn't be good. He was one of thousands who had lost their jobs recently. Although there had been an uptick in online shopping, and more drivers were needed, even more people were waiting to take those positions. He didn't want to wind up in the unemployment lines again.

Thankful he didn't have to work the weekend, he got up early the next day and climbed onto his Harley. Nothing like a good ride to take his mind off the state of the world.

Intending to ride Skiatook Lake's winding roads, he instead found himself heading toward Claremore and the house of the pretty lady. He hadn't even paid attention to her name. His biggest concern had been delivering to the correct address. In the future, he'd make note. And say more. If he spoke too much, though, the stutter he'd worked his life to overcome might leak out...the last thing he wanted to happen. Despite that, the next time he delivered a package to her, he intended to do more talking. And hope his words came out coherent.

Shifting into sixth gear, he opened the engine full throttle. He loved the freedom of riding with the wind in his face. Maybe he could get her to go with him sometime.

As soon as the thought hit him, he squelched it. Getting involved with anyone right now, especially someone on his route, was a bad idea. Still, the woman's image kept bouncing around in his mind.

Jon passed the road leading to her house and kept going. There was no reason for him to go down the dead-end road. Fighting the urge to pull into her drive anyway, he forced his mind back on the highway.

Less than a week later, Jon was loading up his truck, getting ready for the day's runs, when he noticed a package with her address. This time, he took note of her name. Angela Broadhurst. He liked it, and wondered if she went by a nickname. Smiling to himself, he felt a lighter bounce in his step. The day was getting better by the minute.

When he pulled into the drive, disappointment met him with the sight of the empty porch. Feeling deflated, he retrieved her package and jumped to the ground. Then he heard it...

"Ow! You stupid…"

Jon rushed to the side of the house. Angela sat on the ground, surrounded by pulled weeds from an overgrown flowerbed. Her hair was tucked under a straw hat, and dirt smudged her face and covered her sweaty clothes. If she hadn't been cradling an obviously hurt hand, she'd look rather comical.

"Are you all right?"

She yelped and jerked her head toward him as her body stiffened.

"When did you get here?" A radio blaring through an open window had drowned out the sound of his arrival. Craning her neck, she saw his truck in the driveway.

"Uh, j-just a minute ago. I h-heard you yell." Shame clutched his chest at his stuttering. But worse, he felt bad that he'd startled her. Swallowing his emotions, he took a deep breath, then asked, "Can I help you?"

She glanced down and blew a wayward tendril of hair out of her face before looking at him. She relaxed as the corners of her lips tilted upward. "Thank you. I'd appreciate it."

Jon didn't need to be told twice. He pulled up the previously forgotten mask from around his chin to cover his face. Then, in a couple of steps, he was by her side, one hand under her elbow, the other around her waist as he helped her stand. A jolt shot through him. Awareness of her heartbeat, even the pulse in the hollow of her neck, sizzled within him. The urge to embrace her hit him in the solar plexus. Shaking himself, he focused on the more pressing issue and released her.

"What happened?" Blood seeped from a cut on her hand. It didn't look too deep, but it was long.

"Dang Johnson grass. I'd forgotten how stubborn it was." She gave him a sideways glance, then stepped away and moved to the back of the house. She hadn't asked, but he picked up the discarded package and followed, hesitating at the door. Pausing, she narrowed her eyes, giving him the once over, before apparently making a decision and gave a quick nod. "Come on in, if you like. You can put the box on the table."

Jon felt as if he'd just won the lottery and gladly followed her into a modern, airy kitchen. Granite countertops, hardwood floors, oak cabinets and pale yellow walls created a warm and inviting space. She turned down the radio, then headed to the sink and began washing off the dirt and blood. He stood there, as if waiting for permission to speak.

Finally, he cleared his throat. "Well, I should get going. I've got other—"

"Would you mind helping me bandage this first?"

She turned mesmerizing sea-green eyes on him, and he couldn't say no. "Sure."

Reaching into the corner cabinet, she retrieved first aid supplies and set them on the table. "So, what's your name?"

"Jon." Dummy. Couldn't he say more than that?

"Oh, right." She looked at the name on his shirt, screwed up her mouth, then said, "Oops. Guess I forgot how to read."

The way she said it made him laugh. They sat at the table, then she placed a large pad on her hand and he wrapped it with tape. He concentrated on the task, but felt her gaze bore into him. The scents of dirt, antiseptic, and almond shampoo tickled his nose. Her slow, steady breathing filled the charged air.

Surely, she could hear his heart pounding against his chest. Jon had no idea why this woman had such a profound effect on him.

Her voice sounded like a gentle purr when she asked, "Is this your regular route?"

He looked up to find her studying him intently. He hoped his smile reflected in his eyes since she couldn't see his lips. "Yeah. It is."

Her face lit up. "Good. I wouldn't mind seeing more of you." She squeezed his work-roughened hand, then pulled away.

Things were getting way out of control. Time to change the subject. "Have you always lived here?"

"No. I moved back from New York City a few months ago."

"So, no family close by, then?"

"My folks live in a retirement center that's locked down in Tulsa, so I can't see them. I have to admit, I get lonely."

"Don't you have any friends here?"

"I didn't make time initially, then COVID-19 hit." She shrugged as if it didn't matter.

His heart went out to her. "You have one now. If you need anything, call me."

She raised her eyebrows, then gave him a sheepish grin. "I'll do that."

Jotting his number on a notepad, he rose. "I'm behind schedule, so I better kick it into gear."

"Oh, I'm sorry. I didn't mean to hold you up." She stood.

"Don't worry about it. I couldn't ignore a lady in distress. Now, wear gloves when pulling weeds. You do have the right idea, though. You have to get all the roots or else the Johnson grass will come back."

She held up her bandaged hand. "I promise. This is almost as bad as a paper cut."

Nodding, Jon walked out the door and around to his truck without looking back. The green-eyed beauty was too tempting, dirt and all. So much for a lunch break today. That was okay. Angela's smile, alone, was worth it.

****

Angela watched through the windows as Jon made his way to the truck. The feel of his large hands on her small ones had sent shivers down her spine. It had been quite a while since a man held her hand as if it were a cherished possession. Weird. Even though they'd just met, she felt as if they'd known each other for years. She just wished she'd remembered to put her mask on. At the time, though, she'd been in too much pain. Although, he hadn't said anything, so maybe he didn't mind.

Over the next few weeks, the familiar truck brought deliveries on a regular basis. Furnishing her new home and replenishing the flower beds became her pastime. She and the too-cute driver kept their interactions brief, as a general rule, but one day his truck pulled into the drive late in the afternoon. Angela had just taken a batch of cookies out of the oven and tugged off the oven mitt.

Her heart skipped a beat and she swiped at her hair, trying to tuck a few strands back into place. Before he had a chance to step up on the porch, she opened the door. "Hi. Um, if you feel it's safe, I'm okay with you not wearing that." She motioned to the mask he already had in place.

His shoulders relaxed and he tucked the cloth in his pocket.

Oh, man, he is cute! "I didn't expect you, especially this time of day."

He paused, looking uncertain. "I-is it okay? I don't have any other deliveries s-so thought we could visit."

"Of course." *Any time you'd like, sweetie.*

She motioned him inside, but he shook his head. "Can we sit here? I prefer the outdoors."

"No problem. How about something to drink? I have fresh cookies, too." He didn't need to say a word. His smile said it all. A few minutes later, she carried a couple bottles of cold water and the plate of cookies outside to find him sitting in one of the chairs. She had hoped he'd be on the swing so they could sit closer, but reminded herself they didn't know each other all that well. Yet. Placing the cookies on the table between the chairs, she said, "Help yourself."

"Thank you." Jon picked up one of the chocolate chip cookies and took a large bite. "Umm, this is delicious."

"It's nothing. Just run of the mill, ready-to-bake cookies." His compliment warmed her, though.

"Still good." Picking up another cookie, he took a smaller bite.

She waited a moment before making another stab at conversation. "How was your day?"

He dusted crumbs off his hands before responding. "I was distracted."

"Why?"

His gaze slid over her. "Kept thinking about you. Sitting on the swing, the wind blowing through your hair. Just like that first day I saw you."

She blushed, her heart expanding. He'd spent all day thinking about her? She didn't want to admit out loud that she'd been thinking about him, too.

"You know, you remind me of a painting I saw online."

"Seriously?" Her cheeks heated further.

"Yeah. I nicknamed it Oklahoma-California Hippie Girl. The model has long blonde hair like yours and she's sitting astride an old motorcycle." He told her the name of the artist, then paused, as if considering his next words. "Have you ever ridden a bike?"

She didn't hesitate. "Once. When I was younger, I went for a ride on a dirt bike with a guy. He started showing off and wound up wrecking. I broke my arm and swore I'd never get on another one."

Jon's shoulders drooped as his lips turned downward. "Oh."

"Why? Do you have one?"

"Yes. I have a Harley Davidson Touring bike. It's really comfortable and I'm a great rider. If you'd like to go sometime, I'd love to take you."

He looked so hopeful she couldn't tell him no outright. "Let me think about it. Okay?"

The tension tightening his face slid away. "Sure. No pressure."

"Tell me a little about yourself. I don't know anything other than you bring my packages."

As twilight settled around them, they discussed their respective pasts. She told him about working in L.A., and then New York, comparing the big cities to the quiet Oklahoma countryside. Jon told her about his family, where he'd grown up, and how he wound up driving a delivery truck. She even coaxed his birthday out of him. He also admitted he had a stutter that he'd fought to overcome. She'd wondered. Every now and then, he stumbled over his words but for the most part, his speech was fine.

All too soon, he left, leaving her wishing for more time together. Then she looked up the artist on the Internet and found the painting he'd described. She agreed, she *did* resemble the woman sitting on the bike. A smile broke out in her heart. That was what she'd get him for his upcoming birthday. It would be all the sweeter that Jon would deliver his own present.

Two weeks later, the delivery truck pulled into her driveway. Angela had been in the backyard watering, but quickly turned off the faucet and ran around front to find Jon coming from the rear of the truck, a large box in his hands. The framed painting. She had worried it wouldn't arrive in time for his birthday, and relief flooded her to see it finally here.

"Hey, there," she called. "What do you have?"

He lifted a corner of his mouth in the half-smile that kicked her heart into racing mode. "You t-tell me. You ordered it."

Climbing the steps, he set it next to the door. "Want me t-to take it inside?"

"I appreciate the offer, but it'll be fine there. I don't want to hold you up."

His brows furrowed. "Y-you sure? It's kinda heavy."

"Yes, I'm sure. You are coming by this evening, aren't you?"

He grinned. "If you'll have me."

"Good." She gave him a peck on the cheek and the look in his eyes indicated he'd like more. Tonight, his birthday wish just might come true.

A moment later, he drove down the road to her neighbors.

She went to lift the box. It *was* heavy. The oversize package was bulky to boot. Maybe she'd just leave it here and let him bring it in this evening. She giggled at the thought of him having to uncrate his own present, then she returned to the watering.

A few minutes later, the sound of the delivery truck coming back down the road made her smile. When it pulled into her drive, she wondered why. The first thing she noticed when she rounded the corner of the house was that the truck had stopped at the end of her driveway, blocking access to the road. The second thing she saw was an older model white car parked closer to the house and a man exiting the porch.

With the painting!

The man dropped the box and ran toward his car, but Jon caught him in a flying tackle and sent him sprawling. Too stunned to scream, Angela watched, unbelieving. The porch pirate tried to fight, but he was no match for her hero.

Jon hauled him to his feet and slammed him against the hood of the car. Defeated, the man held up his arms in surrender. When Jon glanced up, she finally collected herself enough to pull out her phone and dial 911.

It wasn't long before the sheriff's deputies arrived and took the man into custody. Angela's house hadn't been his first stop as his car was filled with stolen packages. The thief had been smart and hadn't followed the same truck too long before he switched and followed another. She supposed his biggest mistake was following this particular truck down a road with no other way out. If not for Jon, he would have gotten away with it, too. So lost in thought, she hadn't heard his car pull into the driveway.

Once the thief had been taken away and his car towed, Jon wrapped his arms around her and held her protectively. "Are you okay?"

"I should be asking you that. You're the one who tackled the guy. Did you hurt anything when you hit the ground?"

"Naw."

Pride for him swelled with his humble denial. "I'm impressed with the way you picked him up so easily."

"It wasn't anything. Scrawny thing didn't even weigh as much as my bike. Speaking of which, I hope the picture wasn't damaged when he dropped it."

"Picture?"

He chuckled. "Yeah. I checked the sender's address, so I'm guessing that's the print I told you about. And since it *is* my birthday…"

Angela grinned. "You knew."

"Yep. So are you willing to go for a ride with me? As part of my present?" He looked at her expectantly.

How could she refuse? Motorcycles still scared her, but after watching Jon subdue the porch pirate, she knew he'd protect her at all costs. She had moved here to start over, never imagining her new life would be delivered one package at a time by the man of her dreams. And to think, it was all due to a pandemic.

LINDA TROUT

●●●

An Award-Winning and Amazon Bestselling author, Oklahoma native Linda Trout loves Happily-Ever-Afters. When she isn't helping her husband remodel their home, she's outside trying to tame a small portion of their ten-acres (a losing battle). She finds the greatest stress relievers in life are writing a really good scene, and riding her Harley down the highway at 70 mph. Between her six rescue cats, who think they have to help her write, and planning where she wants to travel when the pandemic is over, she's working on her next novel.

Calling Customer Service

by **Bill Wetterman**

Maggie is having trouble with her Kindle. Yesterday, everything on her screen switched to Audible, and Alexa will not read anything but Audible books.

I am a problem solver and say, "Your knight in shining armor will take care of the situation."

I try to access every section of the directions on her Kindle and find nothing I can even understand. As a multitasker, I look for a phone number for Kindle Customer Service and dial, expecting a wait time. Meanwhile, I go onto Kindle Online, hoping to be ahead of the game and ready to see if I can find an answer should their customer service fail to help me.

I find that the phone number is actually Amazon Support and hear a message something like this, "We're sorry for the delay, but due to COVID-19, our call volume has increased. To ensure safety, particularly for the elderly, if you have questions about your Kindle, go to our website for answers, Otherwise, please hold for the next available representative."

Being close to eighty, I am happy they are thinking about the elderly, but I cannot equate the phone call to endangering my safety from COVID. The voice goes on to say, "Your wait time will be approximately forty-two minutes."

Great Scot! At my age, I could be dead before talking to a live person. Undaunted, I put my phone on speaker, set it on the arm of my chair, and concentrate on surfing their website. Their music blared an awful rendition of Magic Carpet Ride by a group I never heard before. The music, if you can call it that, is interrupted every minute by a click, which encourages me that someone might be ready to talk to me. But each click is followed by, "Did you know that with 5G technology and Alexa, you can receive…"

Blah, Blah, Blah.

On the Amazon website, I find a page called Digital Service and Device Support. I have choices like: Change Your Digital and Device Settings, Manage Your App Store Subscription, and Cancel Music Unlimited. None of these will solve my present problem. As I fiddle with the website, I come across a section that says, Echo Family, Alexa Features, Fire Stick, and yes, Kindle E-Readers.

I click on the latter.

Up pops a section asking, Which device do you need help with, Kindle 3rd – 10th Generation, Kindle 2nd Generation DX, or Kindle 2nd Generation?

"Maggie, which generation Kindle do you have?"

"Darned if I know," she replies and brings her Kindle to me for the second time.

Still, on hold, I surf the Kindle for information on what generation it was. I find Wi-Fi settings, Kindle Store for purchasing books, and every other damn thing in the world but what generation it is. If my grandchildren lived closer, I am sure the fourteen-year-old would solve my problem in six seconds, but that is not the case.

I come to a section that says, Find Solutions.

I type, 'How do I remove Audible from my Kindle?' The site takes me to a page of options. Edit Items On Your List. Link and Unlink Your Amazon and Twitch Accounts. Alexa and Alexa Device FAQ's, and so on. I know nothing about what a Twitch Account even is. There is no mention of Kindle or Audible. Meanwhile, I hear a voice emanating from my phone say, "Your wait time is fifty-two minutes. You can go to our website for answers or leave your number at the tone, and one of our agents will call you back when available."

I decide I will leave my number in the hopes of receiving a call back.

Staring at my HP whatever 8GB computer, I think of a brilliant solution. Call the Geek Squad! I am enrolled in every possible Geek Advantage Program. I am sure they can give me an answer. They sell Kindles.

I dial my closest Best Buy and hear something like this, "Welcome to Best Buy. Due to COVID-19, our store hours have been limited. We are open between the hours of ten a.m. and six p.m. For your protection, you must wear a mask and social distance when in our stores. If you have a question for the Geek Squad, go online and talk to the first available agent or follow the directions to make an in-store appointment. If making an in-store appointment, be sure to bring your device with you when coming to our location."

Surprise, I think. No long phone wait time, and I have used the Geek Squad before with good success. On to the website I go. I find and click on 'Chat With An Agent.' I see, 'Hi! I'm your automated Virtual Agent. I'd love to help you. To get started, select a topic or type your question below. You can chat with a live person at any time.'

I avoid the Virtual Agent and go to 'Chat With A Live Agent.' I chuckle. I do not want to talk to a dead one. I wait while four blue circles roll across the bottom of the Chat Screen. No music plays this time—five minutes pass. Why has Amazon not called me back yet? The blue circles are not as irritating as Magic Carpet Ride, so I count my blessings.

Maggie brings me lunch, and I munch. I have been attempting to solve her problem now for a half hour. There is a note on the bottom of my screen that reads, 'Due to COVID-19 wait time will be longer than usual.' Finally, I connect and see, 'Hello, you are connected to Agent Li. Please let me know your email address and the phone number to your account, so I may call you back if we are disconnected.'

I enter both items required. Then the Agent types, 'How can I help you?'

I answer, 'My wife's Kindle is only playing Audible purchased books. We never ordered Audible. How do I remove or fix the problem?'

A note flashes up on the screen. Due to heavier than usual traffic, Agent Li is helping more than one customer, please hold for her response. Five more minutes go by. I find myself humming Magic Carpet Ride and believe I am losing my mind. Then, miracle of miracles, Agent Li types, 'So you are having trouble with your Kindle? Can you describe the problem?'

I just described the problem. Nevertheless, I type. 'My wife's Kindle only reads Audible books as of yesterday. She did not request a free trial of Audible. Her Kindle will not play the book she purchased at Kindle prices.'

The note flashes up on the screen again. I wait. Magic Carpet Ride rolls through my mind, along with some very nasty thoughts. I am now on this call for fifteen minutes and have had plenty of time to finish my sandwich.

Up flashes the words, 'Agent is typing.' I wait. 'Agent pauses.' Then, 'Agent is typing.' I see her note. 'Did you contact Amazon? I asked my supervisor, and she has not had this question before.'

I type, 'I'm a total support customer, including repairs to my refrigerator, stove, and other appliances. Surely, if you sell Kindles, you should be able to problem-solve this.'

I think Agent Li is trying to avoid me. She is again busy with other customers. I am now obsessed with Magic Carpet Ride and singing the original version by Steppenwolf. Agent Li is typing, pausing, and typing again.

A note comes up. 'Agent Li is referring you to a higher level, technical service problem solver. Please wait for Agent Roger.' Another ten minutes go by when a note appears. 'Chat ended.' What?!

Another screen opens, asking me to rate how Agent Li did on the call. I will not share this with any reader. I must have scared my wife with the verbal grumbling coming from my office. She avoids me for an hour.

As a side note, Amazon never calls me back. Talking with my friends, I discover Kindle never speaks to you except to sell you their product. I decide after several other tries to cave in and order my wife two free books each month from Audible and limit her other purchases. After all, due to COVID-19, companies are protecting us seniors, by ignoring us.

BILL WETTERMAN

Novelist: Bill has ten published thrillers and two non-fiction works. His latest, *Christianity Faces the 21ˢᵗ Century,* explores the battle in America today between the progressive cancel culture and traditional Judea-Christian beliefs.

Award Winning Author:
Winner of the Mystery, Suspense, Thriller Competition, OWFI 2011.
Top 10 in the Writers' Digest Genre Fiction Contest 2011 (Over 11,000 entries)
2ⁿᵈ in the Armchair Interviews Thanksgiving Day Competition 2010 (Over 12,000 entries)
Flash Fiction Contest Winner four times this decade, TNW.

Speaker and Educator:
Bill speaks at Conferences, Book Clubs, and Writers' Groups.

Made in the USA
Coppell, TX
21 November 2020